THE NEW BASIC READERS
CURRICULUM FOUNDATION SERIES
REG. U. S. PAT. OFF.

THE NEW
More Friends and Neighbors

The 1956 Edition

*William S. Gray, Marion Monroe,
A. Sterl Artley, May Hill Arbuthnot*

SCOTT, FORESMAN AND COMPANY

Chicago   Atlanta   Dallas   Palo Alto   Fair Lawn, N. J.

Stories

Oak Hill Neighbors

A Horse for Bobby	RUTH LANGLAND HOLBERG	6
Patty Helps Herself	JO MINNER	11
Fun on the Ice	MILDRED COMFORT	16
Fun in the Snow	MARK FRANCIS	20
A Big Surprise	VIVIAN E. LAUBACH	25
Bobby's New Shoes	BLANCHE HEYWOOD	30
Which Circus?	MARJORIE WILLIAMS	36
Wags	CAROLYN HAYWOOD	41
A Trick for Wags	GRACE BLACK	47
Tom's Wish	K. AND B. JACKSON	51

Copyright © 1956 by Scott, Foresman and Company
Previous Copyright, 1952, 1946, 1941, by Scott, Foresman and Company
Philippines Copyright, 1956, by Scott, Foresman and Company
Printed in the United States of America. International Rights Reserved.
Earlier second readers of this Baisc Reading Program were published by Scott, Foresman and Company in 1912, 1913, 1920, 1927, 1930, 1931, 1936, 1952.

Animal Friends
- A Trick on Sandy . . . . . . RUTH BISHOP JULINE . . . 58
- Friends for a Farmer . . . . . ROBERT L. GRIMES 64
- Sleepy Sam . . . . ETHEL C. PHILLIPS 70
- Stop and Go . . . . EDITH ARMSTRONG 75
- The Kitten That Worked . . . ANNE HALLADAY 81
- Home Wanted! . . . . RUTH KERSEY 86
- How Skip Found Joe . . . . . MARIAN WILLARD 92
- The Squirrel's Policeman . . . PATTEN BEARD 97

New Storybook Friends
- Billy Ground Hog Finds Spring GEORGE S. LOOKABAUGH . 104
- Mrs. Goose Forgets . . . . . MIRIAM CLARK POTTER . . 109
- Everything There Is . . . . . MIRIAM MASON 115
- The Old Woman's New Hat . DORIS BATEMAN 121
- Little Mouse Dances . . . . . ELIZABETH UPHAM 127
- The Little Engine . . . . . . MABEL C. BRAGG 133
- The Easter Rabbit . . . . . . DOROTHY BARUCH 139
- Second Helpings . . . . ELIZABETH IRELAND . . . 146
- Mr. Hurry Changes Things . R. O. WORK 152

Friends at Work
- The Two Workmen . . . . . RUTH ANNE KOREY 160
- Molly Plays a Joke . . . . . HENRY BESTON 165
- Aunt Susan's Clock . . . . . MAUD LINDSAY 172
- The Errand Girl . . . . JOYCE LANCASTER BRISLEY 178
- The Birthday Present . . . GRACE AND OLIVE BARNETT . 183
- The New Teacher . . . . . . IRENE U. HARTWELL . . . 189
- Jay's Pumpkin . . . . DOROTHY ARNO BALDWIN . 194
- The Christmas Sled . . . . . JEAN WYATT 199

Old Storybook Friends
- Why the Bear Has a Short Tail FOLK TALE 206
- The Man Who Kept House . . FOLK TALE 210
- The Three Billy Goats Gruff . NORSE TALE 218
- The First Woodpecker . . . . FOLK TALE 223
- A Home in the Wild Woods . . NORSE TALE 228

Oak Hill Neighbors

A Horse for Bobby

"Hello, Mr. Little," called Bobby Wells as he waved to his neighbor.

"I have a new horse!"

"You have?" said Mr. Little.

"Yes! It's in our back yard," said Bobby.

"When did you get your new horse?" asked Mr. Little.

"Just today," said Bobby. "Father says it's a good horse for me. He says it's the best horse on Oak Street."

From *Rowena Carey*, by Ruth Langland Holberg. Copyright, 1949, by Ruth Langland Holberg, reprinted by permission of Doubleday & Company, Inc.

"Is it a little horse about this high?" asked Mr. Little.

"Oh, no!" said Bobby. "It's bigger than that. It's a big, big horse.

It's the biggest horse you ever saw. It's two times as high as you are."

Suddenly Mr. Little laughed. He said, "That's a big horse for a little boy."

Bobby did not answer because just then Mr. Little went into his house.

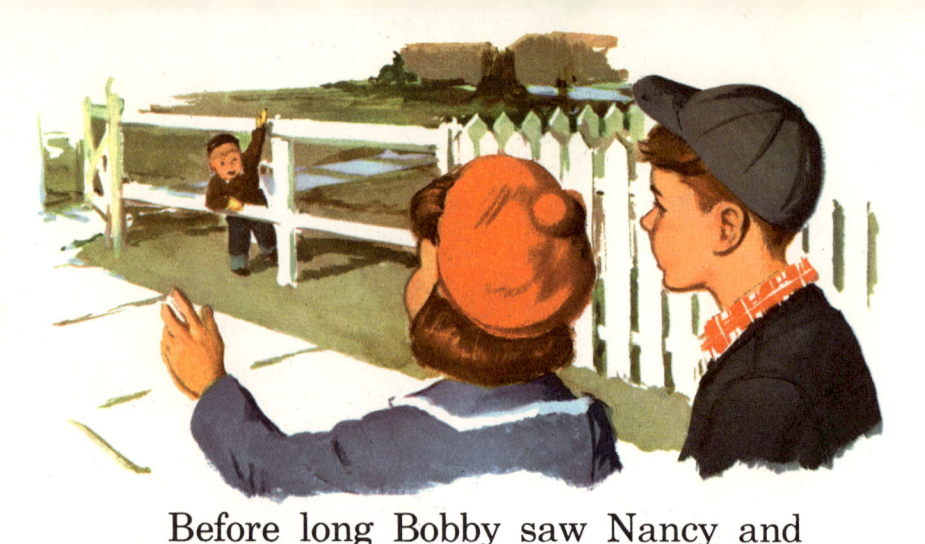

Before long Bobby saw Nancy and Tom Winters coming home from school.

He waved and called, "I have a horse! It's the biggest horse you ever saw. It's two times as high as Mr. Little."

"That's a pretty big horse," said Tom.

"Well," said Bobby, "maybe it's not two times as big as Mr. Little. But it's as big as he is. And it has horns."

"Horns!" laughed Nancy. "Your horse must be a cow. Cows have horns, but horses don't."

Bobby did not answer Nancy because Patty Little came along just then.

"Oh, Patty!" shouted Bobby. "I have a new horse. It's the biggest horse you ever saw. And it has horns. It hasn't any legs, but it can gallop."

"Why, Bobby Wells!" said Patty. "There isn't a horse anywhere that can gallop without legs."

Bobby did not answer because he saw his brother and sister coming.

Bobby waved and shouted, "Come on, Peter and Ann. Come and see my horse."

"What a horse!" laughed Peter.

"It's as big as Mr. Little," said Tom.

"It has horns. But it isn't a cow," shouted Nancy.

"It is a horse that can gallop without legs," cried Patty. "And it's right here on Oak Street."

Bobby did not say anything. He just galloped on his big, high horse.

Patty Helps Herself

"Whatever are you doing, Father?" called Patty. "Why are you watering the garden in the wintertime?"

"I thought you would like to try your new ice skates," said Mr. Little. "Now can you guess what I'm doing?"

"Oh, yes!" said Patty. "The water will turn to ice. I can skate tomorrow."

"Not tomorrow," said Patty's father. "I'll have to put on more water then. You must wait until Saturday."

At breakfast on Saturday morning, Patty cried, "I can skate today!"

"You can try," said her mother with a smile.

Right after breakfast Patty and her mother went out to the garden.

Patty put on her skates in a hurry.

"Here I go!" she cried. But her feet suddenly flew up, and she sat down.

Mrs. Little helped her up, but Patty fell right down again.

"I can't skate," cried Patty. "I can't stand up!"

Just then Peter Wells waved and called, "I'll help Patty skate."

"Oh, fine! Maybe you can pull her across the ice," said Mrs. Little.

Peter pulled Patty across the ice again and again.

"Put one foot in front of the other," he told Patty. "Push your feet along."

"I can't!" cried Patty. "My feet want to go everywhere but in front of me."

"I think you're doing fine," Peter said. "I'll come and help you again tomorrow."

At lunch Patty's father asked, "Did you skate today?"

"No!" said Patty. "I just sat down. But Peter is trying to help me. He is going to help me again tomorrow."

Father smiled and said, "I know how a girl can help herself. Maybe you will find a way to do it after lunch."

Patty was surprised when she went to skate after lunch.

She saw a long clothesline across one end of the garden. It went right over the ice.

14

Patty put on her skates and tried to stand up on the ice. But her feet started to fly out from under her.

Then her hands found the clothesline! "Oh!" laughed Patty. "Father put the line across the ice to help me."

With both hands on the clothesline, Patty began to push her feet along. First one foot, then the other foot.

Before long Patty could skate with just one hand on the line. Soon she was flying along with both hands off the line.

At last she had helped herself.

Fun on the Ice

One Saturday morning there was ice behind the barn at Oak Tree Farm.

The three Winters children were happy. Today they could skate. Some friends were coming to skate with them.

"It soon will be lunchtime," said Tom. "I wish our friends would hurry."

"I wish they would, too," said Nancy.

"Me, too!" puffed little Jack.

His legs were going fast, but his arms were going faster as he tried to keep up.

Suddenly Tom saw his pet calf running out on the ice. Tom waved his arms and shouted, "Get off the ice, Spot! Go back before you get hurt!"

The calf's feet were starting to slide out from under her.

One front foot went this way, and one back foot went that way.

Down she sat with a big bump.

Tom skated over to Spot, and so did Jack and Nancy. They put their arms around the calf and helped her stand up.

All at once the calf's feet went out from under her. Down she sat again!

Down sat the children, too!

Arms and legs waved and wiggled.

Just then Peter and Ann and Patty came with their skates.

"What are you doing?" called Peter with a big smile. "Are you trying to get that calf to skate?"

"No! I'm trying to get her off the ice before she hurts herself," said Tom.

"Oh!" said Patty. "Spot skates like I did at first. She just sits down! Peter helped me, and he can help Spot."

"I pulled you," Peter said to Patty. "But I don't think I can pull Spot."

"Oh, no!" laughed Tom. "But all of us together can push Spot off the ice. Then she won't fall and get hurt."

The next thing Spot knew, she was starting to slide over the ice.

She was not hurt, but she was scared.

"M-a-a!" she said as she went sliding across the ice. "M-a-a! M-a-a-a!"

Fun in the Snow

Oak Hill was in the park at the end of Oak Street. It was a fine place to slide in the wintertime.

Right after lunch one Saturday the children came with their sleds.

Up one side of the big hill came Tom from Oak Tree Farm. Behind him came Jack and Nancy with their sleds.

Up the other side came Peter and Bobby, Ann and Patty.

The children all met at the top of the hill under the old oak tree.

One by one they jumped on their sleds.

One by one they went sliding down the snowy hill.

Then they all walked up.

Again and again the children went sliding down and walking up.

A fast slide down. A slow walk up.

A long, slow walk through the soft, wet snow.

Soon Jack and Bobby stopped sliding and started to make a snow man.

"I'll help," Ann called to the boys. "Wet snow makes a good snow man."

Nancy came to help, too. And soon there was a funny snow man on the hill.

"I'll make a hat for him," said Ann.

Just then she found an old round pan in the deep, wet snow.

"Here is an old pan," she said. "But it is full of holes. No one can use it."

"I can!" shouted Jack. "I'll use it for a sled. The holes won't matter."

Swish! Jack went sliding down in the old round pan.

The pan turned this way and that way. Suddenly it turned over.

Out went Jack into the deep, wet snow. But he was not hurt.

"I'm going next," called Nancy as she ran to pull Jack out of the snow.

One after another the children tried to slide in the funny round sled.

One after another they had to be pulled out of the soft, wet snow.

"This old pan makes a funny sled," said Bobby as he came back up the hill.

Suddenly Ann smiled and took the pan out of Bobby's arms. She put it on top of the snow man's head.

"It makes a funny hat, too," she said.

"What a funny pan!" laughed Tom. "First it was a pan. Next it was a sled. Now it's a hat for a snow man's head!"

A Big Surprise

"Good-by," called Ann as Betty and Bill went up the walk to their house. "I wish I were in your family today."

The children on Oak Street all wished they could be in Betty's family today.

They wished it because today was Valentine's Day.

Valentine's Day in Betty's family was like Christmas or birthdays.

On that day the family always had a party with surprises for each other.

They always had a Valentine Party because their last name was Valentine.

Betty and Bill hurried into the house. Their mother and little sister were busy fixing cookies with red candy on top.

"Oh," said Betty, "those cookies will be pretty for our party at dinnertime."

Bill said, "Let's get red paper and fix the room so it will be pretty, too.

We can run red paper from the light to each end of the room."

As the others worked, little Jane pulled at the paper and said, "Pretty!"

Suddenly Betty cried, "Oh! This room is going to be beautiful!"

Soon Betty got the big valentine box that she had fixed for the surprises.

Mother and Bill got out the surprises. Bill put two surprises in the big box.

Then Mother put in a surprise that had white paper on it. It was tied with red.

"Who will get that surprise, Mother?" asked Bill.

"You will see after dinner," she said.

Next she put in a red-and-white box and another box that was all red.

"Pretty! Pretty!" shouted little Jane as Mother shut the big valentine box.

Then Mother said to Betty and Bill, "I have to get dinner now. Please take Jane and play in another room."

Betty cut out paper dolls. Bill fixed his train, and Jane rolled a ball.

Soon the ball rolled into the next room.

Right after it went little Jane!

She saw the big valentine box and opened it.

She took all the surprises out.

She pulled off all the names.

She was putting the last name back on when Betty came into the room.

"Oh, Jane!" cried Betty. "Don't open your surprise! Wait until after dinner."

Just then Bill came to the door to see what was the matter.

"I can fix things," he said. "I'll put the surprises back in the box and shut it. Then I'll put the box up high."

After dinner Father and Bill handed out the valentine surprises.

The family opened them all together. For a minute no one said a word.

Then Mr. Valentine smiled and said, "My name is on this box. But see what I got. Cake pans!"

Mother said, "What can be the matter? See what I got. Toys!"

Bill and Betty laughed. They knew what was the matter.

"See what we got," they shouted.

Little Jane just waved her surprises and cried, "Pretty! Pretty!"

Bobby's New Shoes

"I wish I had shoes like Peter's," said Bobby one morning. "I wish I had some shoes with big high tops."

"I must have my shoe now," said Peter. "I'll be late for school if I don't hurry."

"Bobby must have new shoes soon," said Mother. "We will buy them today."

Right after lunch they went downtown, and Mother bought new shoes for Bobby.

"Now!" said Bobby. "I have shoes with big high tops like Peter's."

"I must have new shoes," said Mother.

The man opened and shut box after box of shoes. Mother tried on shoes, and Bobby waited. He sat and sat and sat.

Suddenly Bobby could not sit and wait for his mother any more.

His big high shoes started making big high steps. Away they walked with Bobby's feet inside them.

Left foot up! Right foot down!

Big high steps!

Left, right! Left, right!

Big high steps across the floor!

Bobby walked right out of the store.

Left, right stepped the new shoes along the sidewalk. Left, right! Left, right!

Bobby came to the end of the walk and turned the corner. Then he began to count his steps.

"One, two! One, two!" he counted.

He turned corner after corner, but he did not count the corners.

Soon Bobby and his fine new shoes came to the corner of a busy street.

A policeman was sitting there.
He watched as Bobby Wells
walked along, lifting each foot up high.

Then he called, "Little boy! Lift up
your head. Watch where you are going!"

"I am," said Bobby. "I'm watching
my new shoes and counting my steps."

He lifted one foot to show his shoe.

The policeman smiled and asked,
"Where is your mother, little boy?"

"At the big store where we bought
my new shoes," said Bobby.

33

Suddenly Bobby looked around.

"I don't know where I am," he said.

Bobby was lost, but it did not matter. He knew that the policeman would not let anything happen to him.

The policeman said, "What's the name of the store where you bought the shoes?"

"I don't know," said Bobby.

All at once a funny thing happened. The policeman lifted Bobby right up in front of him.

Then another funny thing happened. The policeman took off Bobby's shoe.

"Oh, please don't let my new shoe get lost," Bobby said.

The policeman looked inside the shoe and read the words "Bell's Shoe Store."

"Oh!" he laughed. "Now I know where your mother bought your fine new shoes. That is where we will go."

Off went the policeman with Bobby riding in front. They went riding down the street, riding around the corners, riding to the big shoe store!

Bobby's mother was there in front of the store, looking for him.

"Oh, Bobby," she cried, "how did you happen to run away?"

The big policeman smiled as he lifted Bobby down. Then he said, "Bobby didn't run away. That isn't what happened.

Those fine new shoes that you bought for Bobby just ran away with him."

Which Circus?

A big circus was coming to town! It was coming next week, and that made John Day very happy.

He had saved enough money to pay his own way into the circus. That made him happy, too.

But there was something that made John more happy than ever. He and his father would see the circus together.

Circus pictures were everywhere!

Every circus sign had large pictures of animals and clowns.

Pictures of big yellow lions!

Pictures of elephants and bears!

Pictures of big fat clowns!

Pictures of funny little clowns!

When John shut his eyes, he could see those elephants and clowns doing tricks.

"I'm glad that circus day comes at the end of next week," he thought. "I couldn't wait more than a week."

Just then John heard someone calling.

"Come to the circus with us, John," called Bill Valentine.

"It isn't until next week," said John.

"Oh!" said Peter. "Bill isn't talking about the big circus. We are going to the little circus that came last night."

"I saved my dimes for the big circus," said John. "It has elephants and clowns."

"But it won't have a merry-go-round," said Bill. "This little show has one, and we're going to ride on it now."

John did not say a word for a minute.

At last he said, "I guess I won't go. I'll wait for the real circus next week."

John watched as his friends ran off. Then he heard the merry-go-round, and he knew that he wanted to ride on it.

John took his money out of his pocket. He looked at all the dimes he had saved. Suddenly he ran after Peter and Bill.

At the big merry-go-round John paid a dime and went riding with his friends.

He paid another dime for another ride. He paid a dime for a balloon. Then he saw Bill and Peter going into the show.

John counted the dimes he had left.

"I have enough money for this show," John thought. "I'll go to it. A week is too long to wait for the real circus."

So he paid his money and went inside.

A pony was jumping. Dogs were doing tricks that made John laugh.

Soon John stopped laughing.

There was just one clown in the show.

There were no elephants at all.

John was not happy as he walked home. When he got there, he told his father about the merry-go-round and the show.

"That wasn't the real circus you had saved your dimes for," his father said. "That was just a dog and pony show."

"I know," said John. "I'm sorry I didn't save my money for the real circus. I wanted to go with you."

John's father smiled at him and said, "We can see the circus train come in.

We can see all the big elephants and other animals come off the train. We can see them parade to the circus ground.

That won't take any money at all."

"Good!" said John. "Maybe a parade will be as much fun as the real circus!"

Wags

For a long time Molly Good's home was in a big building right downtown.

In the building there was a sign that said "No dogs or cats please."

Every time Molly saw the sign, she would say, "I wish I could have a dog. A nice little dog to play with!"

One day Molly's family moved to a house near the end of Oak Street.

Many children lived on Oak Street. But Molly did not know them, and she did not play with them.

She wished more than ever that she had a little dog to play with.

Soon a wonderful thing happened.
A letter came from Molly's uncle.
It said that Molly's uncle had to be away from home for a long time.
He could not take his dog Wags with him. So he wondered if Molly would like to have the dog.
Molly's mother asked, "Does the letter say what kind of dog Wags is?"
"It does not say," answered Father. "But a dog named Wags would be little. A little dog is just what Molly wants."
"Yes, I think Molly could have fun with a little dog," said Mother.
"Then Molly gets Wags," Father said.
Molly did not say a word. She shut her eyes and hopped up and down.
That very night a letter was on its way to Molly's uncle. The letter told him that Molly would like to have Wags.

Wags did not get there for many days, and the time went slowly for Molly.

When she saw children playing, she would say, "Soon Wags will get here. Then I'll have someone to play with."

At last one day her mother said, "Oh, Molly! Wags will be here soon. You must get things ready for him."

"Oh," said Molly. "I must get Wags a basket to sleep in. Does he have to have other things, too?"

Mother said, "The men at the pet store will know. Let's go ask them."

At White's Pet Store one of the men showed Molly sleeping baskets for dogs.

"Oh, this one is too big," she said. "But that little basket will be just right for my little dog to sleep in."

Next Molly found a small pan for food.

Then she asked, "Does a little dog have to have any other things?"

"Yes, he does," laughed one of the men. "Any dog must have something to eat."

So Molly got a big box of puppy food.

After Mother paid for all the things, they went back home to wait for Wags.

That night Wags came in on a train. One of the men at the station telephoned to Molly's father.

"Your dog is here," he said. "I can't bring him out. I don't want to leave him here all night. Could you come for him?"

Molly thought Wags would be sleepy. So she got Wags' basket. Off she went with her father to get her little dog.

At the station Molly ran up to one of the men and asked, "Where is Wags?"

Just then something in the station made a noise like a lion.

"What on earth is that?" asked Father. "It can't be a lion!"

The man said, "What did you come for?"

"For a dog," said Mr. Good. "We came for a little dog named Wags."

"Just wait!" laughed the station man. "I'll bring little Wags in here."

Soon the station man came in, bringing the biggest dog Molly had ever seen.

At first Molly just stood without saying a word. Then she walked slowly over to the dog.

"Hello, Wags," she said.

Wags was so happy to find a friend that he began to wiggle all over.

Molly put her arm around the big dog.

"Oh, Wags!" she laughed. "You can't sleep in this basket I bought. But the floor of my room will be big enough for you."

A Trick for Wags

Molly was trying to get Wags to do a trick. Molly would roll a ball and say, "Bring it here, Wags!"

Sometimes Wags would bring the ball to Molly, but sometimes he just stood.

Once in a while he would look around as if he did not hear Molly at all.

Bill and Betty were watching.

All at once Bill said, "Oh, Molly, I know a good trick for dogs. I saw it at the dog and pony show last spring."

Bill told Molly about the dog that had skated on four roller skates.

"I wonder if a dog could skate on just two roller skates," said Bill.

Molly ran and got her roller skates.

It took the children a long while to get Wags on them.

At last he stood with his front feet on the roller skates. Then Molly began to pull him along the walk.

But Wags sat down. Just his skates rolled along behind Molly.

Wags barked and barked at the skates.

"Stop, Wags! Be quiet." said Molly. "Everyone in town will hear you bark."

After a while Wags stopped barking.

Then Betty said, "I wonder how we can keep the roller skates on Wags."

"I know!" cried Molly. "I'll tie them."

Soon the roller skates were tied on.

Betty pushed Wags as Molly pulled.

Suddenly Betty fell, and Wags jumped.

The skates stayed on, but they banged into each other.

Wags began to bark again.

All at once Bill shouted, "I know what to do!

Molly can pull Wags. Betty can push. And I'll keep him from falling."

Slowly they went along the sidewalk. Now Wags could roller skate!

But he skated with two feet rolling, and two feet running to keep up!

As Wags skated faster and faster, Bill cried, "He's a real trick dog!

If he had skates of his own, we could all skate together this summer."

Tom's Wish

Tom Winters sat on the back steps and looked over the quiet farmyard.

School was out, and it was time for summer work on the farm.

"I don't like farms in the summer," Tom thought. "I don't like to hoe weeds.

Hoe weeds! Hoe weeds! That's all I do. I wish I never had to hoe another weed."

Tom was so busy thinking that he did not hear his father come outside.

Father said, "I have news for you, Tom. Uncle Dick has gone to the city to buy things for his store at Four Corners.

He will be gone two days.

He wants you to stay at the store with Aunt Sally while he is away."

For a minute Tom wondered if he could be hearing right.

Then he stood up and said, "Boy! No weeds for two days. Let's go!"

When they got to the country store, Aunt Sally and her cat were resting.

"I'm glad you came to visit," she said.

After Tom's father left, Aunt Sally said, "I'll rest for ten more minutes, Tom. You look around if you want to."

Tom wanted to do more than just look.

He wanted to sniff the good smells in the store.

So he started to walk around.

He hurried right past the chicken feed and the hoes and rakes and shovels.

He hurried past potatoes and cabbages.

He stopped to sniff some red apples.

Then he began to walk slowly past the cakes and the cookies. They looked very good, and they smelled wonderful. So Tom stood there for a long time.

At last he came to the candy, and there he saw an ice cream sign.

"Oh!" thought Tom. "I didn't know that Uncle Dick's store had ice cream this summer!"

"Now!" said Aunt Sally as she put the cat down. "I have been resting long enough. I must get busy."

"Can I help you?" Tom asked.

"Working in this store would be fun."

"Yes," said his aunt. "You can bring me some cans of corn."

Then she smiled to herself.

"Anyone who works here and helps me may eat anything he wants," she said. "And he may eat as much as he wants."

For the second time that day Tom wondered if he could be hearing right.

"Boy!" he thought. "This is nice work! I can eat while I work. I can eat all the candy and ice cream I want. I can eat them whenever I please!"

So Tom ate while he worked.

He ate cookies while he brought the corn to Aunt Sally.

He ate candy while he cleaned the floor.

He ate ice cream while he rested.

Tom ate all day. But he did not eat much of the dinner Aunt Sally fixed.

"Thanks," he said. "I'll eat tomorrow while I work and while I rest."

But next day he did not want candy. He did not want cookies or ice cream. He did not want lunch when it was ready.

Soon Uncle Dick came from the city, and Mrs. Winters came to get Tom.

On the drive home he was very quiet.

When he got there, he walked slowly to the garden. There were lots of weeds in the potatoes. So he started hoeing.

He hoed all the way across the garden. After a while Nancy called, "Dinner!"

"Dinner so soon?" Tom said to himself. "But now that I think of it, I'm hungry."

"Coming!" he called, dropping his hoe. "Save lots of everything for me. I'm as hungry as a bear!"

Animal Friends

A Trick on Sandy

Early in the summer Big Jim Fox came to work at Oak Tree Farm.

Sandy came, too.

Sandy was Jim's dog. He was just a puppy, and Jack Winters thought it would be fun to play with him.

But Jack did not get to play with Sandy very often.

All day long Sandy stayed with Jim. He went riding in the wagon with Jim. He ran after Jim in the fields, and he went with him to feed the animals.

When Jim went to feed the pigs, he always told Sandy to stay outside the pen.

But one morning when Jim stepped inside the pigpen, Sandy ran past him.

Past Jim and into the pen ran the dog! What a grunting and barking there was!

"Uh-uh! Uh-uh! Uh-uh!"

"Bow-wow! Bow-wow!"

Sandy ran after the grunting pigs, and they ran after Sandy.

Around and around inside the pen ran the puppy, barking and barking.

Around and around ran the fat pigs, grunting and grunting and grunting.

All the time Big Jim was shouting, "Stop, Sandy! Come here!"

Suddenly the puppy gave a queer bark as if he were hurt. He went running across the pen on just three legs.

Big Jim took Sandy to the house.

When he got there, he called Jack and pointed to the puppy's left front foot.

"Sandy's foot has been hurt," Jim said.

"A pig stepped on it when Sandy ran into the pigpen. He must stay quiet until his foot is well."

Big Jim tied up Sandy's foot. Then he went back to work.

Jack brought Sandy some cool water.

"You must be quiet until that bad foot is well," said Jack. "You must stay here in the yard with me."

Jack took care of Sandy for many days.

He petted the puppy and brought cool water to him often.

The puppy played with Jack. But he did not try to use his bad foot.

At last Jim said, "Sandy's foot is well. It won't have to be tied up any more."

The next day Jack and Sandy went with Jim to drive the cows to the barn.

"Look," said Jack, pointing to Sandy. "He doesn't walk on that bad foot. It isn't well."

"It's well enough to use," said Jim. "Sandy will soon walk on all four feet."

When Big Jim came in from the field at five o'clock, Jack said, "Oh, Jim! I've been trying all day to get Sandy to walk on four feet. But he won't."

"Well!" said Jim. "Maybe I can get Sandy to use that foot. I'll play a trick on him. I'll tie up his other foot."

When Jim put Sandy down, Jack said, "Look! There he goes! But he's walking on just three feet. He won't walk on his right foot now.

That's queer. His right foot isn't hurt. But maybe he thinks it is hurt because it's tied up. Is that the trick?"

"That's it," laughed Big Jim.

"We will leave his right foot tied up for a while. Just long enough for Sandy to find out that his left foot is well."

The trick worked! Before long Sandy was running on his four good feet.

Friends for a Farmer

"Bob—white! Bob—white!"

"Listen to that bird!" cried Nancy.

"I've been hearing it all week," Tom said. "What kind of bird is it?"

Big Jim listened. Then he said, "He is saying his name. Can you tell what it is?"

The children were quiet as they listened.

"He's saying 'Bob White,'" Nancy said. "What does Mr. Bob White look like?"

"There he is now," said Jim, pointing. "I'm glad to see him. He helps farmers by eating bugs and weed seeds."

"Is his nest in that tree?" asked Tom.

"No," said Big Jim with a smile. "A bobwhite's nest is on the ground."

"Is the nest in that field of hay?" asked Nancy.

"Maybe," said Jim. "If it is, I am afraid I'll run over it tomorrow when I cut the hay. That would be too bad."

"Oh," said Tom, "we will find the nest for you in the morning. Bill and Betty will be here then. They can help us."

Like all good farmers, Tom and Nancy were up early the next morning. But Bill and his sister did not come early.

Tom sat in the cool yard, waiting and wondering why his friends were so late.

At last a car turned into the driveway and honked.

"Hello!" Tom called to Bill and Betty. "Where have you been all morning?"

"Coming to your house!" said Betty.

"We couldn't take the road that goes past the park. There was a bad place in it. We came to a detour sign, and Mother had to take another road."

"That's right," said Bill. "The detour was longer than the other road. So it took us longer to get here."

"Well," said Tom, "you're just in time to help Nancy and me. We want to find a bobwhite's nest in the hayfield."

On the way to the hayfield Tom told Bill and Betty about the bobwhites.

"They are a farmer's friends," he said. "They eat weed seeds and lots of bugs. Bugs in fields! And bugs in gardens!"

While the children were looking for the nest, they heard some queer cries.

"Quit, quit! Quit, quit!"

Tom pointed to a bobwhite flying near the ground.

"That's the mother bird!" he said. "She's making all those queer cries!

Jim says that a bobwhite often cries like that. She is making those cries to keep us from going near her nest."

Just then Nancy cried, "Here is the nest! It is full of eggs! We must show Jim where they are!"

"We must not wait here," said Tom. "That bird won't quit making those cries and come back to her nest until we leave."

Bill said, "If we go far, we may miss Jim when he comes to the field."

"I know!" said Betty. "Let's put a sign here for Jim. A detour sign!"

"Fine!" said Tom. "I'll get the wood."

"I'll get some paint," said Nancy.

Bill said, "I'll put the word DETOUR on the sign in big letters. You have to have DETOUR on a detour sign."

Jim was cutting the hay by the fence when he saw the detour sign.

"That's queer," he thought. "I've never seen a detour sign in a hayfield before."

Jim quit working and walked quickly to the sign. Then he laughed.

"Well!" he said. "I'll be glad to detour around this nest. I think Mr. Winters will soon have some new friends to help him by eating bugs."

Jim was right. In one more week the bobwhite family was busy eating bugs in the farmer's field.

Sleepy Sam

The days had been getting longer and longer and hotter and hotter. Summer had come!

In summer there was one cool spot at Oak Tree Farm. That cool spot was under a big tree on top of a hill.

On every hot day old Sleepy Sam stood there slowly swishing his tail.

Sam was an old horse that had worked for a long time at the farm. But he had quit working. He just rested all day long.

One hot day he heard two girls talking. He swished his tail slowly and listened.

Nancy and her friend from the city were coming up the hill.

Nancy waved and called to her father. When he came to the fence, she asked, "May Kitty and I ride Sam? Kitty has never tried to ride a horse."

"Where are you going?" asked Father.

"We want to go to Uncle Dick's store at Four Corners," answered Nancy.

Father smiled and said, "Old Sam can take you that far, but not very fast.

The hotter the day, the slower he goes. Don't try to make him trot or gallop."

Quickly Father got the old horse ready for the girls to ride. Then he pointed to the highway and said, "Keep off that road. People drive too fast on it.

Take the old road through the woods. It isn't the shortest way to Four Corners, but it goes there."

The girls went riding off on old Sam. Down the long, pleasant road they went.

Right in the middle of the cool woods, old Sam stopped to rest.

"Oh, dear!" said Kitty. "If Sam goes to sleep, we will never get to the store!"

After a while Sam walked slowly on.

By and by Kitty said, "Look, Nancy. I see a red brick chimney sticking up through the trees. Is that the store?"

"No," answered Nancy. "I think it's a farmhouse."

Sleepy Sam walked on and on.

"There's a store," Kitty shouted.

"The red brick chimney we saw is on that country store!"

"Yes," laughed Nancy. "And there is Uncle Dick. What a joke on me! I've been here often enough to know where Uncle Dick's store is. But I've always come a shorter way."

"Hello!" called Uncle Dick.

"Come in and have some ice cream."

Before the two girls could get down, Sam did a queer thing. He turned quickly and started back the way he had come.

Sam opened his mouth and lifted his head.

"Hee-ee!" he said and started galloping.

Bumpety, bumpety, bump went the girls. Bumpety, bumpety, bumpety, bump!

Before they knew it, they were home.

When Father saw them, he said, "My! I thought you would stay longer!"

"Oh!" said Nancy. "Sam played a joke on us. He turned around and came home. He isn't as slow as you thought."

"No," laughed Father. "Sam goes fast when he is coming home to rest."

Stop and Go

Trot, trot, trot, trot came a pony to Oak Tree Farm.

Behind the pony rolled a red cart.

In the cart sat David Wood.

"Oh, David," shouted Jack, "you have a new cart! You have a fine new cart for Trot!"

When Jack quit shouting, David said, "This isn't a new cart. My father had this cart when he was a boy.

But the red paint is new."

"I want to ride," cried Jack.

"Jump in," said David. "I'll take all of you to Four Corners for ice cream."

Jack ran to ask Father if they could go. Then the children climbed into the cart.

"Let's go, Trot!" they shouted.

But Trot did not go. He stood still in the middle of the driveway.

The sun got hotter and hotter.

David clucked to the little pony, but nothing happened. Trot just stood still.

David clucked again and shook the lines, but Trot did not move.

"This is queer," said David. "Trot has never stopped like this before."

Just then Mr. Winters came along.

He said, "I've been watching Trot from the barn. I think he's listening for the right word to make him go. Let me say my magic word."

Mr. Winters put his mouth near Trot's ear and whispered into it.

The pony jumped! Then away he went!

"I wonder what Father whispered," said Tom. "I guess it was a magic word because it made Trot start so quickly."

Jack said, "I'm glad that Father knew a magic word. But does Trot know the way to the store? This isn't the way to go!"

"Yes, it is, Jack," said Nancy. "But it isn't the shortest way to Four Corners. We always go a shorter way in the car.

This isn't the shortest way, but it's the best way for us to go in the cart."

Soon the children were in the store, eating ice cream.

They told Uncle Dick how Trot stood still and would not go.

"Father said a magic word to Trot and made him go," Tom said. "We should know what it is so we can use it."

"H-m-m!" said Uncle Dick. "I know a word that seems to be a magic word.

People often do what you ask when you use it. Maybe a pony would, too. The word starts with the letters PL."

Tom cried, "I know what the word is. I'll try it if Trot stops again."

Tom wanted to drive on the way home. So David let him hold the lines.

At first Trot went very quickly down the old country road. Soon he began to trot a little slower.

Suddenly he stopped and stood still in the middle of the road.

David took hold of the lines and shook them. But Trot did not move. He seemed like a pony made of wood.

"Get up, wooden pony!" cried David.

Jack laughed and shouted, "Get up, wooden pony! Lift your wooden feet!"

Quickly Tom jumped out of the cart.

He put his mouth near Trot's ear and whispered into it.

Trot started with a quick jump, but Tom got into the cart as it went past.

Trot did not seem like a wooden pony any longer. He went galloping home.

When Tom saw his father, he shouted, "I know what your magic word is!

The pony stopped again, and I used the magic word. I whispered PLEASE in Trot's ear, and away he went.

He went so fast that the long old road seemed like the shortest way home."

Father laughed and said, "PLEASE is a magic word. But I'll tell you a joke about that whisper in Trot's ear.

When you whispered in his ear, you blew in it. And when you blow in a pony's ear, he just can't stand still."

The Kitten That Worked

Play and eat! Wash and sleep!
That is what Penny did all day long.
Penny was Ann Wells' yellow kitten.
Ann was always good to her pet.

She gave Penny fish and cream and other things that a kitten likes to eat.

Ann saved her pennies and bought many toys for the kitten to play with. Often she played games with Penny.

One morning after breakfast Ann was watching Penny wash her face.

"Go on. Wash your face!" said Ann. "That is just what you should be doing.

Wash your face clean. You must wash your coat, too, because Mr. Fall is going to take your picture."

"Mew! Mew!" said Penny as if she were asking, "What is a picture?"

Ann went on talking.

"Our family is going on a long trip," she said. "But we can't take you along.

I'll miss you, but Mother says that I may take your picture with me.

Maybe it will make the trip seem a little shorter."

When the kitten was through washing her face, Ann picked her up.

"Good-by, Mother," she called as she hurried off to Mr. Fall's.

Ann stopped in Mr. Fall's doorway. She saw that Mr. Fall was not ready to take a picture of Penny. He was trying to take a picture of Mrs. Day's baby.

Mr. Fall and the baby's mother were trying to get the baby to stop crying.

The mother waved her handkerchief above her head and said, "Smile, Jill!"

Mr. Fall was holding a wooden clown.

"This clown should make Jill smile," he said. "When her mouth turns up in a big smile, I'll take her picture."

But Jill just cried and cried and cried.

"Mew! Mew! Mew!" said Penny.

Suddenly she jumped out of Ann's arms right into the middle of the room.

Then she began to jump at the clown, which Mr. Fall was still holding.

All at once Jill stopped crying, and the corners of her mouth turned up.

"Kitty, kitty! Kitty, kitty, kitty!" she called in her soft baby voice.

Mr. Fall took a picture of little Jill with her face all smiles. Then he lifted her down to play with Penny.

"I wish I had a kitten or a cat," he said, "It would make babies smile when I take their pictures."

"Oh," cried Ann, "will you keep Penny while I'm away? I'll pay for her food. I've saved lots of pennies and dimes."

Mr. Fall laughed and said, "I'll keep Penny without any pay. She can work for her living by making babies smile."

"How funny!" laughed Ann. "A kitten can work for her living while she plays!"

Mr. Fall took a picture of Penny playing with the toy clown.

Ann took Penny's picture with her on the trip. She showed the picture and told everyone about Penny.

So Ann's long, long trip seemed like the shortest trip she had ever had.

Almost before she knew it, the trip was over. When she went to get Penny, she said, "Oh, Mr. Fall! Everyone liked Penny's picture. Everyone wanted to see the kitten that worked for her living."

Home Wanted!

"Well!" thought Nancy Winters as she peeped into the letter box by the road.

"Mr. Banks didn't have any letters or papers for us. So he played a joke on us today.

He put a pile of sticks in the middle of the letter box."

Quickly Nancy knocked the sticks out of the box and ran back to the house.

"Mother! Oh, Mother!" Nancy called in a laughing voice. "Mr. Banks played a joke on us today. He put sticks in the letter box."

"Was the box open?" asked Mother.

"Yes. Just a wee crack," said Nancy.

"Maybe Mrs. Wren played the joke," said Mother. "A wee crack would be big enough for her to get in.
The letter box would be a good home for her. No rain could get in. No crows or cats could get in to eat her eggs."

"Oh!" said Nancy. "I'm sorry I knocked the sticks out. I know that Mrs. Wren worked a long time to bring them."

"Yes," Mother said. "But Mr. Banks has to use the box to hold our letters.
We can put an old can on the fence for a nest. Mrs. Wren should like it almost as well as the letter box."

"Oh, my!" said Nancy the next day. "Here are more sticks in the letter box."

As Nancy knocked all the sticks out, two screaming wrens flew above the box.

"K-e-e! K-e-e! K-e-e!" they screamed.

Nancy said, "Quit screaming and carry your sticks to that old can. You should take the shorter sticks because the longer ones won't go in."

Still the wrens flew around the box. They screamed and screamed at Nancy.

She said to the wrens, "I'm sorry that you can't have your nest in the box. I'm afraid you will go away if you can't."

Then Nancy sat down to think about what she could do.

"I wish the wrens could use the box," she said to herself. "But where would Mr. Banks put our letters and papers?"

Then she cried, "I know! I'll wait for Mr. Banks every day. He won't have to put letters in the box. And the wrens can make a nest where they want it."

The next day Nancy was sitting alone by the road waiting for Mr. Banks.

He met her there day after day.

At last he said, "Playing should be more fun than waiting for me every day."

Nancy just smiled at Mr. Banks.

She wanted to surprise him. So she did not tell him why she came to take the letters every day.

She did not tell him that a family would soon be living in the letter box.

Each day Nancy watched the wrens bring more sticks to the box. Then they began carrying in grass and straws.

They flew off to the field and back to the box, carrying straws. Back and forth. Back and forth. Back and forth.

"Hurry!" said Nancy. "You must carry lots of straws."

At last the nest was ready.

In a week there were six eggs in it.

Then Mrs. Wren sat on the eggs.

Mr. Wren flew back and forth, carrying bugs for her to eat.

One day Nancy heard bird voices inside the letter box. Mrs. Wren's eggs had cracked open. Her babies were out!

How excited Nancy was! How she wished Mr. Banks would hurry!

When he came, he said, "I'm glad you're here today. Your box won't hold all the things I have for your family."

"No!" said Nancy. "It won't hold any of them. Peep through the crack and see why."

When Mr. Banks opened the box, he said, "It's full all right!"

And it was. It was full of baby wrens.

How Skip Found Joe

Skip was Joe Day's dog.

Joe often said to his brother John, "Skip is the best dog on Oak Street.

He has the shortest legs I ever saw on any dog. But he can run fast.

He is smart, too. He almost talks."

When Joe said that, Skip would wag his tail and bark.

Skip's bow-wow seemed to be saying, "Yes, I am smart!"

One Saturday Skip went with Joe and his brother to visit Tom at the farm.

The three boys played games and went sliding down the hay in the barn.

Skip went off alone to run after rabbits. He was not back at five o'clock, and Joe had to go home without him.

After a long while Skip got tired of trying to catch a rabbit. He came back to the barn, looking for Joe.

Joe was gone!

Skip sniffed the cracks in the floor. He barked at the hay above his head. He ran out of the barn, barking as loud as he could. But he could not find Joe.

Skip was very tired. He ran slower and slower and slower. His barks were getting shorter and shorter and shorter.

He wanted his supper. But he was not going home to supper without Joe.

"Skip, come to supper," Tom called from the house.

The dog almost knocked Tom over as he ran in through the kitchen door.

But Skip did not eat supper. He ran from the kitchen to the living room, sniffing at all the chairs. One chair smelled like Joe, but Joe was not on it.

Back and forth ran the dog.

At last Tom pointed out the door.

"Go home, Skip! Go home!" he said.

But Skip would not start home.

"Oh, Skip!" said Tom. "You are not as smart as Joe thinks you are. He said you would go home when I told you to."

Skip listened to Tom with a queer look in his eyes. He always went home when Joe said, "Home, Skip."

But Joe was not here!

Just then Tom ran out of the kitchen to answer the telephone.

Skip followed Tom out of the kitchen. He followed him into the living room. He sat by the chair while Tom talked.

Suddenly Skip lifted his ears.

Joe's voice was coming through the telephone, and Skip was excited.

Tap, tap! Tap, tap, tap went his tail on the floor.

"Bow-wow! Bow-wow!" he barked as loud as he could.

Then he jumped up on the chair.

Skip was excited and happy! He was so excited that he almost knocked the telephone out of Tom's hand.

"Listen, Skip," Tom said. "Joe wants to talk to you. Are you smart enough to know what he says on the telephone?"

Joe's voice called, "Home, Skip! Suppertime! Come home to supper."

How excited Skip was! He barked one loud bark into the telephone.

Off the chair he jumped! Then out the kitchen door he ran.

Soon Skip was at home on Oak Street.

"Smart dog!" Joe said.

"Smart dog!"

The Squirrel's Policeman

"Chatter, chatter" went a voice in the maple tree. A mother squirrel was sitting there above Bill's head.

Bill was glad that a squirrel family was living in the maple tree.

He liked to watch the five babies playing together. He liked to hear Mrs. Squirrel chattering to them.

He liked to think she was saying, "Hurry! Do what your mother does!"

Day after day she chattered, "Do what your mother does!"

That is how she helped her babies learn the things they should know.

Soon four of the squirrel babies could follow their mother up and down the maple tree. Before long they were going up and down alone.

One baby was very, very slow to learn. He was not as big as the other babies. So Bill named him Tiny.

Tiny seemed to be afraid to follow his mother. He seemed afraid to go up and down the maple tree alone.

All summer long the old squirrel chattered to her tiny baby.

By the end of summer Tiny had
learned to go up and come down
the tree alone.

Then fall came. The days were cool,
but the babies had lots of soft gray hair
to keep them warm.

They were learning to jump from
branch to branch in the maple tree.

Four of the babies soon could jump
almost as far as their mother.

It took Tiny much longer to learn.

By and by he, too, could jump from
branch to branch in the maple tree.
But Tiny always was the last one
to jump.

One windy day leaves were blowing all over Bill's yard. And nuts were dropping from a tree across the street.

It was time for the little squirrels to learn to hide food for the winter. Now they could start hiding nuts.

Bill was making a pile of leaves with his rake when Mrs. Squirrel ran past.

Her five babies were following her. They were all running across the street to the big nut tree.

Tiny was last. Before he was across, a car came swishing toward him.

Suddenly Tiny saw a place to hide. Down he jumped into a deep hole.

The hiding place was wet and dark!

Tiny tried and tried to climb up the sides of the deep hole. But he went sliding down again every time.

The poor squirrel was scared, and he began to chatter as loud as he could.

Bill heard the loud chattering noise. When he peeped down into the hole, he saw where poor scared Tiny was hiding.

Quickly Bill pushed his rake down toward the squirrel. Then up the rake climbed the poor little baby.

Up from his cold, dark hiding place he climbed. Up toward the street above! Up toward Bill!

Up into the sunlight came Tiny.
Right into Bill's warm hands!

"Ch-ch-ch!" chattered the poor baby.

For a long time he shook all over.
It seemed he would never get warm.

As soon as Tiny was warm again,
Bill took him across the street.

Mrs. Squirrel came running to them.

Her excited chattering seemed to say,
"Put my baby down!"

Bill talked to her as he put Tiny down.
In a quiet, friendly voice Bill said,
"Stop your chattering, Mrs. Squirrel.
I wasn't hurting your poor baby.

I'm his policeman. A real policeman
helps people. I was helping your baby
better than you could yourself.

When I grow up, I am going to be
a real policeman. But I don't have to
wait until I'm big to help a squirrel."

New Storybook Friends

Billy Ground Hog Finds Spring

"Hello, Mr. Caw Crow. Is spring here yet?" asked Billy Ground Hog.

"Just this minute I waked up from my winter's sleep. I'll go right back to sleep if spring isn't here yet."

"Caw, caw, caw, caw!" said the crow. Then he began to laugh. He laughed until he almost fell off his branch.

"What's so funny about my asking if spring is here?" asked little Billy.

Mr. Crow just laughed some more.

"Oh, pooh, Mr. Crow!" Billy said. "I'll ask someone who isn't so silly."

Soon Billy met some ducks and geese.

"Hello!" he called in a friendly voice. "Has spring come yet?"

"Quack, quack, quack!" said the ducks.

"Honk, honk!" said the geese.

Then they all began to laugh.

At last one old gray goose said, "Oh, Billy! You can answer that!"

"Yes," quacked a duck. "You can answer that yourself."

"Pooh!" said Billy as he walked away. "Pooh! I don't care what ducks and geese say. Ducks and geese are silly!"

Soon Billy met Grandfather Turtle.

Billy thought that the turtle would not laugh at him. So he said, "Is spring here yet, Grandfather Turtle?"

Hiding a smile, Grandfather Turtle answered, "If you don't know, who does?" Then the turtle laughed right out loud.

Billy walked away from the turtle. He wondered why the crow, the geese, the ducks, and the turtle laughed at him.

Just then he heard a lot of noise in the woods.

"Jay! Jay!" screamed some bluejays.

Tap, tap, tap went some woodpeckers.

Billy said, "I'll ask those bluejays and woodpeckers if spring is here yet."

When Billy asked the bluejays and woodpeckers, they laughed at him, too.

"Of all things!" said one woodpecker.

Another woodpecker said, "Why would a ground hog ask if spring has come?"

Poor Billy walked on toward home.

"Pooh, pooh!" he said.

"Pooh, pooh to everyone! I won't talk to any more silly animals.

I should run into my warm home and go back to sleep. But I'm not sleepy."

Suddenly he heard the sound of voices.

"Hello, young Billy Ground Hog," called Mr. Bluebird in a friendly voice. "I'm very glad to see you out today."

"Why?" asked the little ground hog. "Why are you so glad to see me?"

"I was afraid we hadn't been wise," said Mr. Bluebird. "I was afraid we had come back to the woods too early.

But here you are! So spring is here. Ground hogs don't wake up and play in the woods until spring comes."

Now Billy Ground Hog knew why he was not sleepy. He knew why everyone had laughed at him. Now the sound of Billy's laughing filled the woods.

At last Billy knew that he, himself, was one of the signs of spring.

Mrs. Goose Forgets

Early one morning silly Mrs. Goose came knocking on the schoolhouse door.

She came knock, knock, knocking with one end of her big blue umbrella.

Miss Gray Squirrel, the teacher, heard the sound and came to open the door.

"Come in, Mrs. Goose," she said. "Come in and make yourself at home."

Miss Squirrel pointed to a chair, but Mrs. Goose was too excited to sit down.

She waddled about as she said, "I just came to ask—. I came to ask—. Now what was it I came to ask?"

Mrs. Goose looked down at the string on her neck and said, "Oh, dear me! I forgot what I wanted to ask.

I tied this string on my neck so that I wouldn't forget. But I forgot anyway.

I know it was about something that young animal children learn at school."

The friendly teacher said, "They learn to read storybooks. Did you want to ask about reading a storybook?"

"No, no, no, no, no!" said Mrs. Goose, still looking at the string on her neck. "I can read as well as you can yourself.

And I can count. Just hear me count. One, three, six, four, two, five, ten!"

When Mrs. Goose was through counting, she said, "I can sing, too!"

The friendly teacher asked, "Can you sing as well as you can count?"

"Just hear me sing," said Mrs. Goose.

Her singing was very bad. It was so bad that all the animal children put their hands over their ears.

Suddenly Mrs. Goose stopped singing.

"Oh, I forgot!" she cried. "I forgot that I left apples boiling on my fire.

If those apples burn, I can't fill cans with apple butter for the winter."

Mrs. Goose waddled out the door, carrying her big blue umbrella.

She got home before the apples burned and made her apple butter.

Again Mrs. Goose looked at the string on her neck. She picked up her coat and hat and umbrella. Then she waddled back to school.

"What are all the young animals learning now?" she asked.

The teacher said, "I'm teaching them to paint roses. Would you like for me to teach you how to paint a rose?"

"You don't have to teach me that," said Mrs. Goose. "Just see for yourself what a fine rose I can paint."

Splash, splash, splash went the paint!

The rose that poor Mrs. Goose painted looked more like a cabbage than a rose.

Soon the animal children began to write.

"Oh!" said Mrs. Goose. "I almost forgot that I must write something.

I always put names on the cans I fill with food for winter. I must hurry home and write the words APPLE BUTTER."

Mrs. Goose waddled toward the door. Then she waddled right back again.

"Now I know why I tied this string on my neck!" she cried. "I want to ask how to write the word BUTTER. I want to know how many T's are in it."

All at once she began to squawk and wave her umbrella in the teacher's face.

"What is the matter with this school?" she squawked as she waved her umbrella.

"You teach all the children to read and write. But you never teach them to write the word BUTTER. How am I to know how many T's are in it?"

"Oh," said the teacher, "my children learned to write that word last winter."

"Two T's!" shouted all the children.

Then Mrs. Goose quit squawking. She became as nice as she could be.

"Thank you," she said with a smile. "How wise and kind you are! I'm sorry I squawked those loud squawks at you."

Then she waddled out the door, saying to herself, "Two T's! Two T's!"

She hurried home and began to write APPLE BUTTER as fast as she could.

This time Mrs. Goose did not forget.

Everything There Is

Tim was a little goat that had never been outside his pen in the barnyard.

There the big yellow sun was warm and bright. Trees were always blowing in the wind. Woodpeckers drummed on the barn. Often a parade of baby ducks went quacking across the barnyard.

Tim liked to see those pretty things and to hear all those pleasant sounds.

Tim liked to sniff good smells.

He liked to taste things, too. But all he had ever tasted was milk, green grass, and hay that Johnny gave him.

From *Hoppity*, by Miriam Mason.
Copyright, 1947,
by the Macmillan Company and used with their permission.

One day Farmer Zeke let young Tim out in the yard to play with Johnny.

They played until they were hungry. Then Johnny went in to eat lunch, and Tim began to taste things.

He tasted some weeds by the fence. But he ate only a few of those because he soon found a way into the garden.

"M-m!" he said as he tasted a head of cabbage and a few ears of green corn. "I want to taste everything there is!"

Just then Farmer Zeke came running to take young Tim back to his pen.

The next day the farmer said to Tim, "You may play with Johnny again today. But if you are wise, you won't eat anything that you shouldn't."

The little gray goat was not listening. "New things to taste!" he thought.

Tim soon saw a few bright red flowers in the back yard. He filled his mouth with flowers, and they tasted very good.

Then above his head he saw something. It was the same red color as the flowers.

As Tim tasted it, Mrs. Zeke screamed, "You bad goat! Let my coat alone!"

Then she put Tim back in his pen. For two days he tasted nothing new.

On the third day Farmer Zeke said, "Perhaps you will be good now, Tim."

Farmer Zeke let the goat out and went to the house to eat breakfast.

Tim followed the farmer. He saw him sit down before a big pile of pancakes.

Suddenly Tim heard Mrs. Zeke shout, "Oh, dear! The cows are in the road!"

Out to the road ran the family, and into the kitchen ran Tim.

He sniffed the good pancake smell.

"I must taste a few of those things that smell so good," he said.

When the family came back, Tim was eating the last pancake.

After that Tim was shut in his pen for a week. When the farmer let him out, Tim did not taste a thing in the yard.

He just stood in the warm sunlight. He saw the flowers blowing in the wind. He listened to the sound of many voices in the house.

At last Tim peeped in an open window.

He did not see people, but he did see a bed with hats on it. Beautiful hats! Hats with feathers! Hats with flowers!

"I must taste those," he thought.

In through the window he went, and up in the middle of the bed he jumped.

Just as Tim tasted the last hat, a bee came buzzing into the bedroom.

"Oh, good! Here's something that I've never tasted before," Tim thought.

He opened his mouth, and in went the bee.

The bee tasted hot! Burning hot!
The goat's mouth became very hot!
Tim danced and jumped. He hopped up and down in the middle of the bed.
Then he opened his mouth and let out a squeaky cry. He let the bee out, too.
Right then young Tim said to himself, "I'll never taste anything new again!"
And he never, never did.

The Old Woman's New Hat

Old Mrs. Wise always was smiling and never was sad. She had a brick house. She had lots of flowers. And she had a straw hat with a red feather on it.

Every time she went out, she put on her hat. But one day she could not find it.

The old woman looked in every box and under the chairs and under the bed.

Her hat with the red feather was lost!

Right then and there poor Mrs. Wise quit smiling and became very sad.

Mrs. Wise was sad for only a while. Soon she was smiling the same as before.

"It's queer that I lost my hat," she said. "But I won't be sad.

I can get a new hat with a feather. Perhaps a hat with a yellow feather would look better than the one I lost.

Miss Ellen made my old hat. She can make me a new one by tonight.

I'll stop and see Miss Ellen on my way to the store. But I can't go to see her without taking some flowers."

Mrs. Wise found a large flower basket. Out into the bright sunlight she went to fill the basket with flowers.

"I'll cut some of every kind," she said. "I'll have only a few of the same color."

At last the flower basket was filled.

Taking it with her, Mrs. Wise walked out toward Christmas Tree Road.

A squeaky old farm wagon came along while Mrs. Wise was shutting her gate.

Her neighbor, Mr. Bright, was taking chickens and pigs to town in his wagon.

When the gate banged shut, the horse jumped at the noise. And the wagon turned over.

Mrs. Wise screamed. Pigs grunted and squealed. Chickens squawked.

One squealing pig became so excited that it ran down the middle of the road.

Mr. Bright became so excited that he danced around and shouted, "Stop! Stop! All of you stop!"

The runaway pig went on running away.

The pig in the wagon went on grunting and squealing.

The chickens went right on squawking.

All that loud squawking and squealing excited Mrs. Wise. Suddenly she turned her flower basket over her head and started after the runaway pig.

The basket was upside down, and most of the flowers fell out. Only one pretty pink rose stayed in the basket.

How queer Mrs. Wise looked with a pink rose peeping out over her ear!

But she did catch Mr. Bright's pig.

After taking the squealing pig back, Mrs. Wise went on her way.

She was so proud of catching the pig that she forgot all about her basket.

It was still upside down on her head.

The pink rose was still over her ear when she came to Miss Ellen's gate.

"Good afternoon!" called Miss Ellen. "What a pretty new straw hat you have!

It's the only hat I've seen like that. The pink rose looks nice by your ear. You must be proud of that hat."

Mrs. Wise put her hand up to her head. There was her basket upside down! There was a pink rose over her ear!

"Well," she thought, "if an upside-down basket looks like a hat, perhaps it is!

If Miss Ellen thinks so, other people will think so, too. If most people think it's a hat, I can think the same thing."

Mrs. Wise was smiling a proud smile as she walked toward the village.

"Well, well!" she said. "It just shows that we should always be smiling and happy and never be sad. Never be sad, no matter what happens!"

Little Mouse Dances

Once a merry little brown mouse lived in a tiny house on the very top of a hill.

This merry little mouse liked to dance.

Each morning she put a red paper rose over her ear. Then she began to skip and dance and sing.

She danced most of the day, singing,
"Why rub and scrub
All day in the house?
It's better to dance
Like Little Brown Mouse."

One afternoon Grandmother Mouse came to visit. She looked all around.

Then her squeaky old voice said, "My! What a lot of dust! You should rub and scrub and clean your house."

"Not this afternoon!" said Little Mouse. "I'll clean my house tonight. I want to dance and sing this afternoon. I will rub and scrub and clean tonight."

Out of the house and through the gate she ran. Then down the grassy hill she danced as if she had wings on her feet.

At the foot of the hill there was
a village. In the village there was
a store window with a red dress in it.

When the little mouse saw the dress,
she said, "I'm sure that pretty dress is
the same color as my rose. I'll buy it."

She bought the dress and put it on.
"I'm proud of this beautiful dress,"
she said. "I'm sure to get it wet if
I rub and scrub in it. So I just won't
scrub tonight. I'll dance in the village."

Little Mouse danced most of the night
in her new red dress. She danced and
danced as if she had wings on her feet.

Grandmother Mouse came to visit Little Mouse again the next afternoon.

Dust lay on the table. Dust lay under the table. Dust lay on the bed. Dust lay under the bed. Dust lay in all the cracks in the floor.

Grandmother Mouse said, "There still seems to be a lot of dust in this house. Perhaps you didn't have time to scrub."

"No," said the mouse. "But I'm sure to have time to scrub and clean tonight. I must go to the village store now."

Out the gate and down the hill she ran. In the store window lay some shoes. Little Mouse saw that the shoes were the same color as her dress and her rose. So she bought the beautiful red shoes.

She danced all afternoon and most of the night in her new shoes. She danced as if she had wings on her feet.

It was late when the mouse waked up.
She looked at her new dress.
She looked at her red shoes, which lay on the table beside the bed.
Taking them from the table, she said, "My, my! There is such a lot of dust on these shoes. I'm not proud of them. I can't dance in these dusty shoes."
The little brown mouse began to rub the shoes. Soon they were pretty again.
She blew the dust off the flower.
She blew on the dress and shook it.
How bright the dress and the rose and the shoes looked then!

Suddenly the little mouse wanted her tiny house to look the same way.

She began to scrub and dust.

"I'll have plenty of time to dance when my work is done," she said. She flew about as if she had wings on her feet.

When the work was done, she put on her red dress, her flower, and her shoes.

Then around the table she danced as if she had wings on her feet.

She sang in her squeaky mouse voice,
"It's better to scrub
All day in the house
And dance at night
Like Little Brown Mouse."

The Little Engine

Once a farmer had some fine wheat. He took his wheat to a station where a long train of cars was standing.

He filled every car with wheat.

When that was done, the farmer said, "Please carry my wheat to the city."

The cars all answered, "We will be glad to carry your wheat for you. But cars cannot move alone.

We must have an engine to pull us. We must have a good engine to pull such a long train to the city."

By the station was a big green engine. It had only a few cars to pull.

The farmer thought, "That big engine doesn't have to work hard. Perhaps it will pull these cars of wheat."

So he called to the engine, "Will you pull these cars to the city? My wheat must get there before dark tonight."

The big green engine did not like hard work. It liked only easy work. Pulling cars to the city was not easy.

So the engine moved away from the station, screaming, "No-o-o! No-o-o! No-o-o! That's too far for me to go."

The farmer went to a big red engine, which stood nearby.

"You are such a large engine," he said. "It will be easy for you to pull these cars of wheat. I'm sure you will do it.

The wheat must go to the city to be ground into flour.

The flour will be made into bread.

Then all the people will have plenty of bread to eat this winter."

The red engine surprised the farmer. It backed away from the station, calling, "Puff! Puff! I have worked enough!"

The poor man called to a third engine, which was standing near the station.

He said, "Please pull these cars filled with bags of wheat. The bags of wheat must get to the city tonight before dark.

The wheat will be ground into flour.

The flour will be made into bread.

Then all the people will have plenty of bread to eat this winter."

This engine was a lazy, lazy engine. It would do only very easy work.

It took one look at the long train of cars filled with bags of wheat.

Then the lazy engine's bell called out in a very lazy way, "Too long, too long!"

"Oh, dear!" said the sad, sad farmer. "Where is an engine that will take all my bags of wheat to be made into flour?"

Just then a squeaky little engine came bumping and banging along.

"I'll take the bags of wheat," it said. "I'll get your bags of wheat to the city before six o'clock tonight."

"Fine!" said the farmer. "But it won't be easy for such a little engine to pull such a long train. Are you sure you can?"

The engine said, "I'm not lazy. I have done hard work for years and years."

So it pulled hard, and the cars filled with bags of wheat rolled slowly away.

Soon the engine came to a high hill. Up it started. It puffed and pulled and puffed harder and harder and harder.

As it pulled, it sang, "I think I can—I think I can—I think I can—"

Up, up, up, up went the little engine, pulling harder and harder all the time.

It kept on singing, "I think I can—I think I can—I think I can—"

Slowly and surely it pulled to the top. Then it hurried down the other side.

Faster and faster it rolled down the hill. Now it was singing, "I thought I could! I thought I could! I thought I could!"

Soon the engine's work was done, and all the bags of wheat were in the city.

Then the wheat was ground into flour. The flour was made into bread, and people had plenty of bread that winter.

The Easter Rabbit

A little white bunny with pink eyes sat all alone, talking to himself.

"I want to be an Easter Rabbit this year," he said. "How can I?"

No one answered. So he began to cry. But while Bunny was crying, he kept one eye open to see if anyone was coming.

"If I cry hard enough, surely someone will tell me how to be an Easter Rabbit," he said. So he cried harder. He cried until he heard a wee sound.

"Buzz, buzz, buzz!"

Honeybees were flying by on the way to their hive. As they flew, their wings made a soft buzzing noise.

When the last honeybee was almost
to the hive, Bunny called to it,
"Please stop and tell me how
To be an Easter Rabbit now!"
As the bee flew on to its hive, it said,
"My hive must have a lot of honey.
So I can't stop and help a bunny."
Bunny watched until the bee was inside
the hive. Then he began to cry again.
But he kept one pink eye open as before.
He cried until he heard a wee sound.
"Squeak, squeak, squeak!"
A mouse ran squeaking along the path
toward the village.

"Perhaps that mouse can tell me how to be an Easter Rabbit this year," thought Bunny. So he quickly called,
"Please stop and tell me how
To be an Easter Rabbit now!"
The mouse kept on going along the path. As it ran past Bunny, it squeaked,
"I must keep going on my way.
I've plenty of things to do today."
Bunny cried harder and harder. But he still kept one pink eye open. He cried until he heard a sound above the path.
"Tweet, tweet, tweet!"
A robin was singing from a leafy branch.

She looked down from the leafy branch and said, "Tweet, tweet, tweet, tweet.

You are not very smart, little bunny. Surely you know that wishing and crying have never helped anyone yet.

Surely you know that a crybaby rabbit could never be an Easter Rabbit. Do not cry and be sad. Sing and be gay!"

Bunny asked, "What should I sing?"

"Tweet, tweet, tweet," sang the robin. "Sing anything. Just sing and be gay."

Bunny started to sing.

"That's much better," said the robin. "Soon you will be as gay as can be."

Bunny sang as hard as he could until the robin said, "Stop! That's enough!

Now find a snowdrop and eat it.

Then wiggle your nose and both ears.

Next rub the back of your fat neck with your left front foot.

Last of all hop on your two back legs and wiggle both of your front legs.

Then you will meet a beautiful fairy!"

Bunny said, "I can't find a snowdrop. There isn't any snow on the ground."

"Use your eyes," said the gay robin.

Suddenly Bunny saw a tiny flower as white as snow, growing by the path.

"Perhaps that's the snowdrop I should eat before I meet a fairy," said Bunny.

So he ate it as quick as could be.

He wiggled his nose and both ears. He rubbed his fat neck. He hopped on his back legs and wiggled his front legs.

All at once a leaf blew into the path.
Dancing on the leaf was a tiny fairy.

The fairy had bright stars everywhere.
Stars in her hair. Stars on her dress.
Stars on her wings. She was holding
a tiny stick with a star on the end of it.

The fairy kept on dancing and dancing
and dancing on the leaf.

"Oh!" thought Bunny. "She's the fairy
that I am to meet. I wish she would
stop dancing. Then I could ask her how
to be an Easter Rabbit this year."

But the fairy kept dancing. So Bunny
was very quiet and did not say a word.

At last the gay fairy quit dancing.

"Hello, nice little bunny!" she said.

"I know what you want to be this year. So I'll touch you with my magic star and change you into an Easter Rabbit."

She touched Bunny's head, his back, and two of his feet. Suddenly he had a red hat, a blue coat, and two red shoes.

"Am I an Easter Rabbit?" he asked.

"Not yet," said the fairy.

She touched one of Bunny's front feet with her magic star. Then Bunny had a basket of candy eggs!

"Thank you, kind fairy," he said. "Now I can hide eggs for the children in the village. An Easter Rabbit always hides Easter eggs."

Second Helpings

Every woman in Maple Village baked good things to eat. But Mrs. Smart baked really wonderful things.

Her rolls were as light as feathers. Sometimes they blew away if they were not eaten at once.

So she tied strings on them, and they flew around her kitchen like balloons.

Mrs. Smart made wonderful cakes, too. She was always making a new kind.

One afternoon she took butter, eggs, flour, milk, and honey. She cut up a few apples and cracked a few nuts.

Then she made a new kind of cake.

The new cake smelled so good that Mrs. Smart telephoned some neighbors.

"Meet me for supper tonight in the park," she said. "Meet me by the boat pond."

"Fine!" they said. "We will meet you by the boat pond at six o'clock."

Near sundown the neighbors met by the pond where the boats were.

Mr. and Mrs. Small had a basket filled with food and cold drinks.

Mr. Bell said, "I didn't bring things to eat or drink. I have a red balloon and a blue balloon for May and Tommy Small."

Mr. Gay did not say what he had.

Mrs. Small began taking food and cold drinks from her large basket.

She put chicken, bread and butter, cold milk, and ice water on the table.

Everyone began eating and drinking.

Soon Mrs. Smart asked, "Is everyone ready for my apple-and-nut cake?"

"Oh, dear! Not I," said Mr. Bell. "I've eaten too much now."

"So have I," Mr. Small said. "I have eaten too much, and I've been drinking too much milk. I really can't eat cake."

"Now!" said Mr. Gay. "We can use what I brought to this party. I brought my fiddle. You men can surely eat cake if you do a little dancing first.

I'll play my fiddle while you dance.

It's time I did something to earn my dinner. I'll earn it with my fiddle."

Soon merry sounds filled the park.

Mrs. Small picked up a pan and used it for a drum. She drummed and drummed.

Mr. Gay fiddled and fiddled and fiddled. The other two men went dancing around the table with Tommy and his sister.

At last Mrs. Smart said, "You have fiddled and drummed and danced enough. You can eat cake now! Mr. Gay has earned his cake by this time."

She cut some cake for each neighbor. But she gave Mr. Gay the biggest helping because he had earned it.

After the people had eaten their cake, they washed their hands in the pond.

As they came back from the boat pond, Mr. Bell said, "That was the best cake I've ever eaten. What kind was it?"

"Upside-down cake," said Mrs. Smart. "Why are you walking on your hands?"

Mr. Bell asked in surprise, "Me? Walking on my hands? So I am!"

"So are the others!" cried Mrs. Smart. "Their feet almost touch the branches of the trees. Tell me why you are all walking on your hands?"

No one could answer Mrs. Smart.

Suddenly she cried, "My cake is what did it! All of you ate upside-down cake. All of you are walking on your hands.

I'm the only one on my feet. I haven't eaten any cake. I haven't had time."

"The cake!" shouted Mr. Gay.

"The cake is surely what did it! Now we need to get changed about. How shall we get right side up?"

"I know!" said Mrs. Smart. "Each of you must eat another helping of cake.

You will turn upside down again, but you will really be right side up!"

She began to feed cake to everyone. One by one they turned right side up.

"I'm surely glad I had plenty of cake," Mrs. Smart said. "And the next time I have upside-down cake, I shall be sure that everyone gets two helpings at once."

Mr. Hurry Changes Things

Mr. Hurry lived on a farm.

Behind his barn was a very tall hill. Behind the very tall hill was a forest of maple trees. In the maple forest was his henhouse full of hens.

Each day Mr. Hurry went to the forest, taking food to his hens and water for them to drink.

He had to go up the tall hill, down the tall hill, and into the maple forest.

One day Mr. Hurry said, "Fiddlesticks! This trip really takes too long. I shall change things. I'll move this tall hill."

Away he hurried to Neighbor Black's.

"Mr. Black!" he said. "I need to move the tall hill by my maple forest. May I use your digging machine to move it?"

"You surely may," said Mr. Black. "I earn my living by digging ponds with my machine. Moving a tall hill will be easy work for my digging machine."

He brought the machine to the road and told Mr. Hurry how to start it.

"Look!" he said. "Touch this and put your foot on that."

"I see," said Mr. Hurry.

"Now!" said Mr. Black. "I shall teach you how to drive this machine. And I shall teach you to work the big shovel."

"Not yet," said Mr. Hurry. "Just let me learn to start the engine first."

The two men changed places.

Mr. Hurry touched this and put his foot on that. And the engine started!

Then he touched something else.

Away toward Mr. Jolly's garden went the machine and Mr. Hurry.

"It's moving!" he called to Mr. Black. "How do I stop it? Run fast and tell me!"

Mr. Black ran, but he did not catch up.

"Fiddlesticks!" said Mr. Hurry. "I can find the thing that stops this machine."

He saw something that looked like a long stick, so he gave it a hard pull.

The big shovel dropped down and began to dig up the earth in Mr. Jolly's garden.

"Help! It's digging!" cried Mr. Hurry. "Some beehives are right in our path!"

Quickly he pushed the stick. Up came the shovel, and the beehives were in it. Off went the machine, carrying the hives.

Angry bees flew out of their hives, stinging and buzzing and stinging.

"Bring back my bees!" called Mr. Jolly. But the machine was moving on toward Mrs. Blue's apple tree. Her cow, Dolly, was standing under its leafy branches.

Mr. Hurry became excited and pulled the stick again. Down fell the hives, and the shovel began digging up the earth.

Mr. Hurry gave the stick a quick push. Up came Dolly, swishing through the leafy branches of the apple tree.

Dolly's angry moo scared Mrs. Blue, who had gone to hoe her cabbage plants.

Mrs. Blue quit hoeing. She screamed in an angry voice, "Put Dolly down!"

The machine was moving into the road, carrying Dolly and a few green branches.

After it ran a long parade of neighbors.

Suddenly the machine ran off the road toward Mrs. Short's henhouse.

Mr. Hurry pulled and pushed the stick. Down fell Dolly. Up came the henhouse.

Away rolled the machine, carrying the henhouse down the road.

Bumpety-bang! Bumpety-bang!

Bumpety, bumpety, bumpety, bang!

Before Mr. Hurry knew it, the machine was moving into his own barnyard.

There Mrs. Short's henhouse fell off.

On went the machine, digging a path across fields of hay and corn and wheat.

The machine stopped at Mr. Black's, and up ran the parade of angry people.

"At last!" shouted tired Mr. Hurry. "I stopped this thing at last!"

"You didn't stop it," said Mr. Black in an angry voice. "It stopped because there is nothing left to make it go."

"Fiddlesticks!" said Mr. Hurry. "I shall fill it and make it go again. I'll move everything back where it was."

"Pooh!" said Mr. Jolly. "I'm tired of honey. Mrs. Blue may keep my bees."

"Good!" cried Mrs. Blue. "Dolly may stay with Mrs. Short. I really think I'll like bees better than a cow. Bees won't eat apples and branches off my tree."

"Oh!" said Mrs. Short. "Dolly can eat grass in my yard. I won't have to cut it. I don't have hens. So I really don't need a henhouse. Mr. Hurry may have it."

"Thanks!" said Mr. Hurry. "I won't need to move my tall hill after all."

Friends at Work

The Two Workmen

Mr. Brown did not work downtown on Saturday.

That was when he fixed things around the house at 110 Oak Street.

On sunny Saturdays he worked outside. He put new boards in the fence. He fixed the back gate so it would open and shut.

On rainy Saturdays he always found something else to fix inside the house.

Whatever Mr. Brown was fixing, Jay was right there helping.

Jay always tried to use his toy saw and toy hammer when he helped. But there was never much he could do with them.

One warm, bright Saturday Jay and his father were building new back steps.

Jay had his toy hammer and his saw. They were not much help, but Jay was.

He helped hold the heavy boards while his father sawed them. He handed Father his big heavy hammer when he needed it.

"You are good help, Jay," said Father. "Someday you will be a fine workman. When you're ten years old, you may have a real hammer and a saw of your own."

"I won't be ten for two years!" said Jay.

"Well!" Father said. "It may take you that long to save money to buy the things."

"Oh, Father!" laughed Jay.

"If I save money for two whole years, I can buy all the hammers in town."

That night Jay counted the pennies and dimes in his bank. Each week after that he saved a few more dimes or pennies.

One day just before noon Jay ran in to ask how soon lunch would be ready.

Jay knew that his mother was washing. He ran through the living room and down the kitchen stairs.

From the foot of the stairs Jay saw a pond of water in the middle of the floor. The pond was getting bigger every second.

In the middle of the pond stood Mother.

"I can't turn the water off," she said. "I telephoned for a man to come and fix the water tap. But he can't come before four o'clock. I don't know what to do!"

"I know," said Jay. "We must shut the water off from the whole house. I've often seen Father do that, and I know what he uses to do it."

Off ran Jay to get the thing he needed. It was heavy, but Jay brought it quickly.

"Look," he said, pointing above his head. "That's where we shut off the water."

"You can't reach that," said Mother. "You aren't tall enough. Here is a chair for you to stand on."

"Now!" said Jay. "All I have to do is turn this round thing to the right."

The round thing was not easy to turn. At first Jay could hardly turn it at all.

"There!" he said at last. "The water is shut off! Now that pond won't get bigger because water can't run from the tap."

That night at supper Jay's mother told his father what had happened.

"It surely was a good thing that Jay knew what to do," she said.

"Jay is a smart boy," said Father with a big smile on his face.

"He has been helping me and learning to do things for a long time. He has been a helper long enough. It's time he had things of his own to work with."

The next afternoon Jay went downtown to meet his father.

They came home with all the things a young workman needs.

Jay was a real workman at last.

Molly Plays a Joke

Hammer and saw! Hammer and saw!
Joe and John Day were making a house out of wooden boxes. The house was to be a place to meet with their friends.

Molly Good had come over. She stood on her roller skates, watching the boys.

"Do you need a helper?" she asked.

"What could you do?" asked the boys.

"I might help you hammer," she said.

"No," said Joe. "Girls can't hammer."

"I might help you saw," said Molly.

"No," said John. "Don't touch a thing. We will be done by noon if we hurry."

Molly skated away on her roller skates.

Soon she thought of something else and came back, smiling.

"Aren't you going to have tables and chairs in your house?" she asked.

The boys did not answer Molly at all. They just began to hammer.

Molly kept right on smiling and talking.

The boys hammered louder and louder. So Molly talked louder and louder.

"You really need tables and chairs," she shouted to the boys. "I might go to the store and get some wooden boxes to use for chairs. Shall I?"

Still the boys did not answer Molly. They just hammered louder than ever.

Molly's smiling face became sad.

"I'll just go to the grocery store and bring back boxes anyway," she thought. "The boys will need boxes for chairs."

Molly took off her roller skates and hurried home to get her wagon.

"The grocery man might give me some boards, too," she thought.

And he did. The grocery man piled two boxes and six boards on the wagon.

Taking all those heavy things home from the grocery store was hard work.

Two boards and a heavy wooden box fell off the wagon at once. So Molly tried to pull with one hand and hold the boxes on the wagon with the other.

But the wagon would not roll straight. And it would hardly go through the gate into the Days' yard.

"The grocery man gave me some boxes for chairs," Molly called from the gate.

"Oh!" cried Joe. "We don't need those wooden boxes. Mother will give us some old chairs and a table."

Then Molly thought of something else to do with the wooden boxes.

"You haven't any stairs yet," she said. "You might use these boxes for stairs."

Joe asked, "Why should we have stairs? This building is only one story high."

"I know," said Molly. "But you might build a second story. You really need an upstairs and a downstairs."

"We haven't time to make an upstairs," said John. He reached for his hammer and started the loudest hammering of all.

Before very long Molly had thought of something else. As quick as could be, she ran to get something she needed.

When she came back, the boys were hammering their loudest. So Molly shouted her loudest.

"Here's paint for the floor," she called in her very loudest voice. "I have a can of dark blue paint and a can of yellow."

Joe said, "We really do need paint, but these cans are only part full! There isn't enough of one color for the whole floor."

"No," said John. "Our floor can't be part blue and part yellow.

Come on, Joe. Let's get a cold drink before we do the rest of our work."

"I'll fool those boys," Molly thought.

"I'll put the two colors together and make green. I'll have plenty of green to paint the whole floor. And I'll do it."

Molly started her painting at the door.

Swish went the paint! Back and forth! Back and forth! Back and forth!

Soon part of the floor was painted.

The whole floor had to be painted before the boys got back. So Molly worked harder and harder.

At last she looked up. She could not move without stepping in wet paint!

Molly shouted her loudest for help, and soon the boys came running.

"I wanted to play a joke on you," cried Molly. "But I played a joke on myself. I painted myself in."

"We will get you out," John said.

"We can't reach you from the door. But we can cut a hole behind you."

John took his saw and began to cut a hole for Molly to step through.

"I was a very bad helper," Molly said. "I'm sorry you had to cut your house."

"Oh!" said John. "We really needed a window. We just forgot to make one.

We never would have thought of it if you hadn't painted yourself in.

Now the floor is painted!

The window is made!

And the house is done by noon!"

Aunt Susan's Clock

"Hello," said Nancy, reaching up to put her arms around Aunt Susan's neck. "Here we are for our Saturday visit."

"Hello, dears," said Aunt Susan.

"I was watching for you. I knew you would come as soon as you had eaten your breakfast.

I knew you would hurry straight down the path to my house for a visit.

So I said to myself, 'I must hurry and start my Saturday baking. Nancy and Jack and Tom will soon be here.'"

"M-m," said Tom as they all went into Aunt Susan's brick house. "There is a wonderful smell in this kitchen!

Let's play a guessing game and guess what's baking in the oven. I say cookies! And I can hardly wait to taste them."

"It might be cake," said Nancy.

Jack did not play the guessing game. He knew that anything Aunt Susan baked in her oven was sure to be good.

"You never will guess what is baking in my oven today," said Aunt Susan.

"It's a surprise, and it isn't done yet. It won't be done until noon."

Tom and Nancy looked quickly toward the kitchen clock above their heads.

Jack could not tell time. So he said, "Noon? Noon? How much longer is it until noon, Aunt Susan?"

"Not very long," she said. "Just watch the clock until the hands meet and point straight up. Then it will be noon."

All three children sat down to watch the clock.

Minute after minute went slowly by. The hands were moving very slowly around the clock's face.

Jack was hungry. He could hardly wait for the surprise. He was soon tired of seeing the clock's hands moving so slowly.

"Hurry up! Lazy, lazy clock!" he said. "You are as slow as a turtle!"

"Oh, Jack!" laughed Aunt Susan.

"A good clock never changes the way it goes. It always goes the same way. Not too fast! Not too slow!"

More minutes went slowly past.

At last Nancy jumped up and said, "Aunt Susan needs a helper. I can't sit and wait until the hands are straight up.

Please give me an apron, Aunt Susan. I'll help wash the pots and pans."

"Fine!" said Aunt Susan. "I can use a helper. Here's a pink apron for you."

"I'll be a helper, too," said Tom. "I'll put the pots and pans away. But I won't need an apron."

Tom and Nancy were good helpers.

Nancy put on the apron and helped with the pots and pans. Tom carried them across the kitchen and put them away.

Jack sat still and watched the clock.

"Will it ever be noon?" he wondered.

Part of the time Jack whispered, "Straight up. Both hands must meet and point straight up. When they meet, the baking will be done."

At last the big hand gave a quick jump.

"Aunt Susan!" cried Jack. "It's noon! Both of the clock's hands are pointing straight up. Is the baking done?"

Aunt Susan said, "Yes. It's noon, and now the baking can come out of the oven."

She reached into the oven and got four big baked potatoes. She carried the baked potatoes to the table.

She reached into the oven again and took out four small apple pies.

"Pies!" shouted Tom. "A pie for each one of us! What a wonderful surprise!"

Aunt Susan carried the four pies to a window and left them there to cool.

Soon a good lunch was ready, and everybody sat down to eat.

When the pies were eaten, Tom said, "It surely didn't seem long until noon. Time really goes fast for busy people."

"Not always," said Jack. "Not when you're busy doing what I was. I was teaching myself to tell time."

The Errand Girl

Molly's whole family was busy.

Her father was busy with a rake in the yard. Grandfather was watering flowers and vines around the house.

Grandmother was in a bedroom upstairs making a coat for Molly. Mother was in the kitchen fixing supper for everybody.

Only Molly had nothing at all to do.

"I need some grass seed," said Father, taking money from his pocket. "I don't have time to get the bag of seed myself."

"I'll do your errand!" cried Molly.

"Please do an errand for me, too," said Grandfather, smiling. "Here are some nickels to pay for what I want.

I need string to tie up the branches of this vine. It must be heavy string to hold such big branches."

Molly took the nickels. Then she called, "Can I do an errand for anyone else?"

"Yes, I have an errand," called Mother. "If you are going to the grocery store, please get some bread for supper."

Just then Grandmother called from the upstairs bedroom, "Oh, Molly! Please get a paper of pins for me."

Grandfather said, "You might forget part of our errands, Molly. Perhaps you should write them down."

"Oh, no," laughed Molly. "I don't need to write them. I won't forget. A good errand girl hardly ever forgets."

Father reached into his pocket to get more money for Molly.

"Here!" he said. "Here is more money to buy groceries and pins."

Molly put pennies, dimes, and nickels into her apron pocket.

Off she went with a hop and a skip to do everybody's errands.

All the way to the grocery store she went dancing and singing,

"Seeds for Father.
Bread for Mother.
String for Grandfather.
Pins for Grandmother."

"Hello," said Molly to the storekeeper. "I want a bag of grass seed."

She paid the storekeeper five dimes, three nickels, and two pennies.

"What else?" asked the storekeeper.

"Some bread," said Molly as she paid the storekeeper a dime and a nickel.

"What else?" asked the storekeeper.

"String," said Molly, taking five nickels from her apron pocket. "It must be strong enough to tie up a big vine."

Then she said, "I've a whole dime left to pay for something. But I forgot what."

"Was it milk or potatoes or butter or other groceries?" asked the storekeeper.

"No! It wasn't groceries," said Molly. "I'm sure it wasn't groceries."

"Well!" said the storekeeper. "If it wasn't groceries, perhaps it was candy."

"I wouldn't forget candy!" said Molly.

Molly sat on some boxes to think what else she had to buy. All of a sudden she saw something tiny and bright that lay on the floor. It was a straight pin.

"Pins!" cried Molly. "Pins! Pins! Grandmother wants a paper of pins!"

"A paper of pins!" said the storekeeper. "I'm sorry, but I don't have pins to sell. Perhaps the storekeeper across the street can sell you some."

"Oh!" said Molly. "I'm sorry you don't have pins to sell. But I'm glad someone carried a pin in here and dropped it. It helped me think of my last errand."

The Birthday Present

It was a warm, lazy day, just right for riding in the country. Tom was riding over the farm on Sleepy Sam.

They made a detour so that old Sam could get a cool drink from Deep Pond.

While Sam was drinking, Tom looked all around. Down in the pond he saw an old turtle and two turtle babies. In a leafy tree he saw a woodpecker flying from branch to branch to get bugs.

As Sam walked on, the day became hotter and hotter. At the old road, he stopped again to rest and cool off.

Tom listened to the soft, lazy sounds. Leafy branches were blowing in the wind. Bugs and bees were buzzing in the vines that covered the fence.

All of a sudden Tom heard loud noises. Honk! Cluck, cluck! Squawk! Bang! Then he heard a man's angry cries.

Tom made Sam trot toward the sounds. A grocery truck had run off the road.

The truck was the small grocery truck that Uncle Dick Gray carried groceries in. It had run into the vine-covered fence.

Uncle Dick stood beside the truck.

"You silly clucking hens!" he shouted. "Why don't you keep off the road?"

"What happened?" called Tom.

"Oh," said his uncle, "I ran off the road to keep from hurting those hens.

My truck didn't touch them. But here I am while everybody waits for things.

Mrs. Wood needs a new clothesline so that she can put out her washing.

Your Aunt Susan is waiting for butter, flour, cabbage, and other groceries.

But I can't get my truck out of here."

Tom said, "I'm strong. I can push."

"Thanks!" said Uncle Dick. "You are hardly strong enough to push the truck. I'll get some men to come and do that."

Tom said, "I may not be strong enough to push. But I'm strong enough to carry groceries and things that people need."

So Tom went riding off. He carried the clothesline to Mrs. Wood. He carried part of Aunt Susan's groceries to her.

The next day Tom was riding along the old road to Four Corners. He was going there to buy a present.

When Sam stopped to rest, Tom cried, "Keep moving! Keep moving!"

He was excited as he ran into the store and said, "Hello, Aunt Sally! I came to buy a birthday present. I worked for Mother to earn money to pay for it."

"A birthday present!" said Aunt Sally.

"Yes," said Tom. "Father's birthday is today. Here are five nickels I earned. Now, please sell me the present."

"What present?" asked Aunt Sally, hiding a smile.

"Oh!" laughed Tom. "I forgot that I haven't told you what I want to buy."

He pointed to a big blue handkerchief that was covered with white stars.

"That's the present I want," he said. "I'm sure Father will be proud of it."

Aunt Sally shook her head and said, "You'll have to pick out something else.

I can't sell that handkerchief for only five nickels. We paid six nickels for it. I have to sell it for more than we paid. That's how a storekeeper earns money."

Tom wondered what to do. He did not have time to earn more money. He would not ask Father to pay for his own present.

"Buy candy for him," said Aunt Sally.

"No," said Tom. "Mother made candy for his party tonight. This handkerchief covered with stars is what I want. It is the only present I really want to buy."

All of a sudden a voice said, "Well! If that's the only present you want, then that's the present you'll have."

Uncle Dick had left his grocery truck in the driveway and had come into the store.

He rubbed his chin for a second or two. Then he picked up the blue handkerchief covered with stars and handed it to Tom.

"You earned this yesterday when you carried the groceries for me," he said. "You didn't think of nickels yesterday. So we won't think of nickels today."

The New Teacher

Today was the first day of school.
It was a busy day for most of the children living in town or in the country.

Breakfasts were eaten fast.

Mothers waved good-by to children as they hurried out gates and driveways.

Up Oak Street hurried Patty and Ann, Molly and Betty. Following the girls came Joe and John, Peter, Jay, and Bill.

Nancy and Jack Winters followed Tom and David through Oak Hill Park.

Wags, Skip, and Sandy wanted to follow the children. But dogs do not go to school—even on the first day.

This year some of the children had a new teacher. But she was not strange to them.

Everybody had often seen Miss Young on the playground. Everybody knew her friendly smile and pleasant voice.

Into the new teacher's room hurried the children. She smiled and said, "Good morning, everybody."

The friendly children smiled right back. The boys smiled as they put away their caps. The girls smiled as they found places to sit.

"This year you will learn many things," said the new teacher. "I shall teach you more about reading and counting. I shall teach you how to write better.

We have a whole year to work hard. Today we shall take our time and get to know each other."

First they all sang together.

Next the teacher read a good storybook.

Then she said, "Let's make pictures."

"What kind of pictures?" asked David.

"Why not make some pictures of me!" said Miss Young with a sudden smile.

Ann whispered to Patty, "I can't do that. I make heads like balloons."

Patty whispered back, "I make noses and chins that are long and pointed."

Miss Young heard the whispers.

She smiled a friendly smile and said, "I'm sure you'll all make good pictures."

Miss Young stood up very straight.

"I'll be quiet. I won't even move while I'm having my picture made," she said.

As soon as all the pictures were done, Molly came up to be Miss Young's helper. They began pinning up pictures.

When Joe's picture went up, he said, "Oh, Miss Young. I've given you too long a chin. You really have a short chin. Please put up only the best pictures."

"That's just what I am doing, Joe," said the teacher. "I know these pictures are the best that everybody could do."

Miss Young did not look the same in any two of the pictures.

In some she was tall. In others she looked like the shortest woman in town.

In some her hair looked like a black cap. In others her hair was all puffed out.

There were big chins and little chins! Long arms and short arms! Fat necks and tiny necks! Big noses and no nose at all!

As the teacher looked at the pictures, she had a proud smile on her face.

"They all look just like me," she said.

And strange as it seems, they did!

In each picture she had a big, big smile.

Jay's Pumpkin

"Get your cap, Jay," called Peter. "Everybody is waiting for us in the park."

Jay said, "You'll have to go on alone. I must take care of my pumpkin vine."

"We need you," Peter said. "We didn't have enough boys for a game yesterday."

"Well!" said Jay. "I have to take care of my pumpkin vine first. I've taken good care of it all summer. But there is something the matter with it now.

I'm going to water it and look for bugs and pull weeds. If I don't, I might not have even one pumpkin for Halloween."

"I'll help you," said Peter. "You can do the work in a shorter time with a helper."

Peter carried water for the plant.

Jay pulled weeds and looked for bugs.

"My!" he said. "It surely has been hard work to grow this vine. But I have been having fun.

I planted five seeds, but only one plant came up. Before long the tiny plant branched out and ran along the fence.

More and more branches grew until the vine almost covered the ground.

Then lots of big yellow flowers grew on the branches of the vine. And next came little green pumpkins."

After Jay had taken a bug from a leaf, he said, "I've taken very good care of my vine. I've given it plenty of water.

But all of a sudden the pumpkins began to fall off. Now I have just six left."

The next day Jay saw that only five of his pumpkins were left on the vine.

"I hope I can grow five big pumpkins for Halloween," Jay thought.

"I'll give one to my mother for pies. I'll give a Halloween pumpkin to Peter. And I'll keep a big one for myself.

Then I believe I'll sell the others. I can sell them to the grocery man."

But one by one more pumpkins fell off. Soon there was only one left on the vine.

It was hardly as big as Jay's head. No matter how much care that pumpkin was given, it never grew any bigger.

On Halloween morning Peter came by.

"I'm going to the grocery store to buy a pumpkin for Halloween," he said.

"Oh!" said Jay. "I had hoped that I would have a pumpkin to give you."

"That doesn't matter," Peter answered. "I'm sorry only one little pumpkin grew on the vine after you worked so hard."

"I was having fun anyway," said Jay. "Even if I didn't grow a lot of pumpkins to sell or give away or keep for myself."

Just then Mr. Green, Jay's neighbor, called from the fence, "Oh, Jay! I wonder if you'll sell me your big pumpkin."

Jay wondered why Mr. Green had said such a strange thing.

"What big pumpkin?" he asked.

"The one in my yard," said Mr. Green. "One of the branches of your vine reached through the fence. A pumpkin grew in my yard all summer."

Into Mr. Green's yard ran the boys. They could hardly believe their eyes. There lay a very, very large pumpkin.

"Oh, what a big joke!" shouted Jay in his loudest voice. "I believe I grew the biggest pumpkin in the country. And I didn't know I was growing it!"

The Christmas Sled

"Now, Jane!" said Betty Valentine to her little sister. "What is A for?"

"Apple!" shouted Jane.

"And the letter B?" asked Betty.

Jane shouted, "Ball! And C is for cap!"

Betty was teaching Jane her ABC's from a book Bill had given her for Christmas.

Betty had been her mother's helper for the afternoon. She had taken care of Jane while Mother had scrubbed the kitchen and had gone to the store.

Now Betty was taking care of Jane while Mother got dinner.

When Jane became tired of ABC's, the girls began to color pictures.

Betty laughed when she saw that Jane had given a woodpecker pink wings.

Betty was having a hard time coloring a picture of a village. She kept going to the window.

She was watching the weather. It was strange weather for this time of year.

It had rained the day before yesterday. It had rained yesterday and today.

Each time Betty looked out, rain was splashing down harder than ever.

"Will this rainy weather ever change?" she thought. "Will it ever get colder?"

If the weather changed and got colder, the rain might turn to snow. Then Betty could slide in the park on her new sled.

Soon Jane said, "Please help me make my new duck waddle." So Betty did.

Back and forth waddled the toy duck. Back and forth waddled Jane following it.

The girls were having lots of fun with Waddle Duck when Father came home.

"Do you think this bad weather will ever change and get colder?" Betty asked.

"Yes," said Father. "I believe that our rainy weather will change soon. I believe the weather is colder now."

"I hope so!" said Betty. "I want to slide down Oak Hill on my new red sled."

Next day the weather was much colder. The ground was covered with snow.

Now Betty could slide on the sled that Grandfather had given her for Christmas.

Betty and Father went out together. He tied Betty's warm cap under her chin

"Look," laughed Betty as she pointed to feathery piles of snow on the fence. "The fences have caps today, too."

"Those are strange caps," said Father.

As he started away, he waved good-by.

"I hope you have lots of fun sliding in the park," he called.

Betty had taken only a few steps toward the park when Mother ran out to the gate.

"Oh, Betty!" she said. "The milkman is always very late in snowy weather. Please go to the store and get some milk."

Off went Betty to the grocery store.

After she had paid for the milk, she put it on her sled and started home.

Mr. Green waved as she went by.

"Betty!" he called. "I didn't remember to buy bread yesterday. I can't go out in such cold weather. I wonder if you would please get some bread for me."

"Yes," said Betty. "I'll get the bread as soon as I've taken this milk home."

Betty went home with the milk.

Then she went back to the store and bought the bread.

As she was taking it to Mr. Green, Mrs. Brown called to her.

"Jay has a cold," Mrs. Brown said. "He can't do my errands. Would you please get a bag of flour for me?"

"Yes," said Betty. "I'll get it as soon as I've taken this bread to Mr. Green."

She went to Mr. Green's and back to the store. She had not even started to the park when Bill called her to lunch.

While the family was having lunch, she told what she had done since breakfast.

"You're a fine helper," laughed Mother. "Your new sled is a fine grocery truck for this kind of weather."

Father asked, "Did you get to slide in the park very much?"

"I didn't slide at all," laughed Betty. "But my grocery truck did lots of sliding to and from the store.

I'll do my sliding this afternoon."

Old Storybook Friends

Why the Bear Has a Short Tail

One cold day a hungry bear met a fox who was carrying a long string of fish.

"My!" said the bear. "I believe that is the most fish I've ever seen. Where did you get them?"

Now this fox was sly, like all foxes. He wanted to fool the bear. He did not want the bear to know that he had not caught the fish himself.

"I caught them all," he said, hiding a sly smile. "I caught them myself! All foxes can catch fish. It's very easy for us to catch fish."

"I hope you'll tell me how to catch fish the way you foxes do," the bear said.

"Surely! I'll be glad to," said the fox, hiding another smile.

"Go to the river and cut a hole in the ice. Sit down and put your tail in the water. Then be quiet and wait for the fish to bite.

Your tail may sting and hurt a little when the fish bite. But remember this. The longer your tail is in the river, the more fish you'll catch.

When you think you have caught enough fish, give your tail a quick pull. Be sure to give it a strong pull, too. Now remember all I've told you!"

"Oh," said the bear, "it's a strange way to fish. But I shall do it. And I hope the fish will bite. Good-by, Mr. Fox."

As the bear went away, the fox did not try to hide his sly smile.

At the river the bear made a wide hole in the ice. He sat down and hung his tail in the river.

The water seemed to grow colder and colder and colder. The bear's tail grew colder, too. It began to sting.

The bear believed that fish had started to bite. He wanted lots of them to bite. So he sat very still. But his tail kept getting colder and colder. It kept stinging and hurting.

Late in the afternoon the bear thought that he had caught enough fish. So he tried to pull them out of the river.

The bear could not even stand up!

The water in the hole had turned to ice.

The part of the bear's tail that hung in the river was caught in the ice.

All of a sudden the bear remembered what the fox had told him to do.

After the bear had given a quick pull, he gave a very strong pull. And out of the ice came his tail!

But only part of it came out—and the shorter part at that! Most of his tail was caught fast in the ice.

The sly fox had fooled the poor bear by a mean trick.

All this happened a long time ago.

Since that day all the bears on earth have short tails. All the foxes on earth are proud of the sly tricks they play.

And even to this very day all foxes are as sly as sly can be.

The Man Who Kept House

Long ago there was a farmer who believed that his work was too hard.

Every night when he came to his house on the hillside, he asked the same thing.

"Wife, what do you do all day while I work hard in the fields?"

"I keep house," his wife always said.

The man would say, "That is so easy! I wish I had nothing to do but churn butter, boil porridge, and keep the house clean."

At last one night the man's wife said, "Tomorrow you and I shall change work!"

"Wonderful!" said the happy man.

"Boiling porridge, churning butter, and watching the baby will be easy for me!"

The next day the wife went out to the fields. The man stayed in the house.

First he filled the churn with cream.

All of a sudden he remembered he had not seen the baby since his wife went out.

"This is terrible!" thought the man. "I hope the baby isn't lost."

He looked for her in the yard. Then he ran down the shortest path to the river.

There he found the baby playing in a boat on the bank of the wide river.

The man caught her up in his arms and hurried back to his churning.

When he went into the kitchen, he saw a pig beside the churn.

The pig had knocked over the churn, and the cream was running out.

The man stamped the floor and roared in his loudest voice, "You mean old pig!"

The man's angry cries scared the pig, and it ran outside at once.

The man put more cream in the churn.

But just then he remembered the cow. No one had given her water. No one had taken her to eat grass since yesterday.

"This is terrible!" the man said as he went to get water for the cow to drink.

He carried the heavy churn with him so that the pig could not knock it over.

The man reached for a rope that hung in the well. Then most of the cream ran out of the churn.

The angry man stamped and roared, but he pulled up enough water for the cow.

After he had given her some water, he started to take her to a grassy field.

All of a sudden he remembered that the baby was all alone in the house.

"This is terrible!" thought the man. "She may fall in the fire and get burned! But what shall I do with the cow?"

The man looked up at the grass that grew on the roof of the house.

"I'll put the cow on the roof. She can eat grass up there," he said.

He put a wide board from the hillside to the roof to make a bridge for the cow.

She went across the bridge to eat grass. And the man went back to his churning.

Since it was almost time for his wife to come home, he had to make porridge.

He filled the porridge pot with water and hung it in the fireplace. He started to make a hotter fire to boil the water.

Then he remembered the cow that he had taken to the roof a few minutes ago.

"This is terrible!" the poor man thought. "The cow may fall and hurt herself."

Taking a long, strong rope with him, he climbed to the roof again.

The man tied one end of the long rope around the cow's big horns. He dropped the other end of the rope in the chimney.

When he got back inside the house, he reached up the brick chimney and caught the rope in his hand. He tied that end of the rope around his leg.

"There!" he said. "This strong rope is tied to my leg and to the cow's horns. Now she can't fall. Now I'll make the fire burn hotter and boil the porridge."

Just then the cow fell off the roof!

She hung from the roof by the rope on her horns. There she hung outside the house, crying, "Moo! M-o-o!"

When the great heavy cow fell outside, the rope on the man's leg pulled him up the chimney. There he hung upside down above the porridge pot.

The poor man could not get down! He could not get up! All he could do was roar in a loud, gruff voice.

The man's gruff cries got louder and louder. The cow's angry moos got louder and louder, too.

"What can this mean?" thought the wife as she ran to the mooing cow.

Quickly she cut the rope.

The angry cow dropped down in the yard.

At that very second the wife heard a sudden great splash inside the house.

She ran in and saw the man. There he hung with his legs up the chimney and his head in the porridge pot!

Never again as long as he lived did the farmer try to keep house.

The Three Billy Goats Gruff

Long, long ago there were three goats named Gruff. All three liked to eat grass on the hillside.

They always took the shortest path to the hillside. And the shortest path lay across a bridge over a wide river.

Under the bridge a mean and ugly troll was often hiding. The ugly old troll had a great loud voice. It sounded just like the terrible roar of a lion.

One day Little Billy Goat Gruff started across the wide river.

Trip, trap! Trip, trap! Trip, trap! went his wee feet on the bridge.

"Who is walking across my bridge?" called the troll with a terrible roar.

"It is I," said Little Billy Goat Gruff. "I'm going to the hill to make myself fat."

The mean troll stamped and roared, "No! I'm going to gobble you up!"

"Oh, please don't!" cried the wee goat. "Wait for Big Billy Goat Gruff. He is much bigger than I."

"Be off with you, then," said the troll. "Since you are so small, I'll hide here and gobble up your bigger brother."

After a while the second goat started across the bridge over the wide river.

Trip, trap! Trip, trap! Trip, trap! went his feet on the boards.

"Who is walking across my bridge?" called the troll's terrible voice.

The second goat answered, "It is I. I'm going to the hill to make myself fat."

"No!" roared the ugly old troll louder than ever. "I'm going to gobble you up!"

"Don't gobble me up!" cried the goat. "Wait for Great Big Billy Goat Gruff. He is much bigger than I."

"Be off with you, then," said the troll.

By and by the third goat came along.

TRAP! TRAP! TRAP! TRAP! stamped his heavy feet across the bridge.

"Who is stamping across my bridge?" called the troll in his terrible voice.

The third goat answered, "It is I. It is Great Big Billy Goat Gruff. I'm going to the hill to make myself fat."

The ugly troll jumped up on the bridge.

He roared in his loudest voice, "Oh, no! I've been hiding since morning, waiting for you. I'm going to gobble you up!"

Great Big Billy Goat Gruff just shook his great big horns at the ugly troll.

"Just try to gobble me up!" roared Great Big Billy Goat Gruff. Then he banged right into the ugly old troll with his great big horns.

Down into the wide river fell the troll. Down he fell with the most terrible roar that has ever been heard.

That was the end of the ugly troll!

After that the three goats grew so fat they could hardly walk. And if the fat has never dropped off, they are very fat yet.

The First Woodpecker

Long, long ago in a faraway village there lived a very ugly woman.

She was never kind to anyone.

One afternoon she was baking a cake. She believed she was alone in her house. But all at once she heard someone moving.

Turning quickly from the oven, she saw a strange old man standing behind her.

"I have not eaten since yesterday," the strange man said in a friendly voice. "I hope you'll give me a bite of cake."

Smiling a sly smile, the woman said, "Perhaps—when my little cake is done."

When the cake was taken from the oven, the woman thought, "I'll keep this cake. It is much too large to be given away. I shall bake a smaller one for the man."

An ugly, sly smile was still on her face as she looked at the man.

"You'll have to wait," she said to him. "I'll bake a smaller cake."

The man waited while the woman made a hotter fire. He sat and waited while the smaller cake was baking.

When the cake was taken from the oven, the woman's mouth hung open in surprise.

The smaller cake was so large that she had to touch it to make sure it was real.

"My!" she thought. "This was smaller than my apron pocket when I put it into the oven. Now it's as big as my cap.

I can't give such a fine large cake to a strange man. I'll bake a smaller one."

The mean old woman made a cake that was smaller than the second one.

"Surely this will be the smallest cake that anyone can bake," she thought.

While the third cake was baking, the strange man grew even more hungry.

But when the woman saw the cake, it was bigger than the one before!

"My!" she thought. "These cakes grow like magic while they are baking.

This should be the smallest cake, but it's the biggest. It's much too wonderful to be gobbled up by this strange man."

The old man rubbed his hands together. Then he reached for the smallest cake.

"Don't touch it!" screamed the woman. "I won't give you even my smallest cake. You'll find plenty of food in the forest. Go there and eat with the wild animals."

"No!" shouted the man. "You, yourself, shall go to the forest. You, yourself, shall eat with the wild animals.

Since you are too mean to be a woman, you shall be a bird. You shall work hard to find your food in the bark of trees."

The man gave a sudden great stamp on the floor. Then the woman became smaller and smaller and smaller.

The man gave another great stamp, and wings grew out of the woman's back.

At the third stamp her apron and cap and dress changed to feathers.

The mean and sly old woman had been changed to a bird. It had white feathers for an apron and red feathers for a cap.

The bird lifted its wings and flew off.

That was long, long ago.

Ever since that long-ago time, there have been birds with red caps and white aprons.

These birds are called woodpeckers. They find their food in the bark of trees. Their loud cries are heard in the forest, even to this day.

A Home in the Wild Woods

One morning a long time ago a farmer was looking at his sheep.

"Well, well, my fine sheep!" he said. "I believe that you are bigger than you were yesterday. Soon my wife and I will be having you for dinner."

"Pooh!" thought the sheep. "I shall be having something to say about that! I can fool the farmer. I can hide from him. Then he can't eat me."

When the farmer left, the sly sheep hurried straight to the pen of a lazy pig.

"Hello!" said the sheep. "I hope you know why the farmer feeds you so well."

"I don't know why," grunted the pig as he gobbled and gobbled his corn.

"I do," said the sheep. "A minute ago the farmer told me. He said that he and his wife were going to eat you. But I'll help you fool him and save yourself.

We can go away together and hide in the forest. We can build a house of our own in the wild woods."

"Thanks!" squealed the pig. "Let's take the shortest path to the forest at once."

On the way to the wild woods, the sheep and the pig met two geese.

"Hello!" honked the friendly geese. "What are you doing on such a fine day?"

The sheep said, "We are going to build a house and live together in the woods."

"May we go?" asked one of the geese. "Having a home with jolly friends would be pleasant. Most pleasant, I'm sure!"

"H-m-m," grunted the lazy pig.

"Everybody who goes along must work. Can you cut down trees to make a house?"

"No," said the geese. "We can't cut even the smallest tree.

But we can cover the roof with branches and fill the wide cracks with leaves. Then no wind can come in. No rain can come through the cracks and get you wet."

"Oh!" the pig squealed. "I don't want to get wet. Our roof must be covered. Come along with us to the wild woods."

So the four animals went on together.

Soon they saw a proud rooster. "Where are you going?" he asked.

"To the wild woods to build a house for all of us," answered the sheep.

The rooster said, "I hope you'll let me come, too. When a rooster sleeps under his own roof, he crows loudest and best."

"H-m-m!" grunted the pig. "Can you cut down trees and hammer boards?"

"Pooh, pooh!" said the proud rooster. "I'm the smallest one of all. I can't do heavy work. But I'll wake you early, and you'll have plenty of time to work."

The pig squealed, "All right! You can help even if you are the smallest."

The five animals went on together until they came to the wild woods. There they began to build their house.

The sheep cut down ten large trees and made boards. The pig hammered the boards together. The geese covered the roof and filled the wide cracks.

The proud rooster waked everybody early each morning.

The animals were merry as they worked. They were as happy and gay as could be when their house was done. But they did not know that a mean wolf family lived nearby.

Each wolf was mean and ugly.

One morning the biggest wolf said to the smallest wolf, "Listen, Brother! I saw some silly farm animals yesterday in the forest. I'm going to visit them."

Off he started to the new house.

The five friends saw the wolf coming.
They knew how mean a wolf can be.
So they got ready to drive him away.

They opened the door wide and waited.

Soon the wolf stepped through the door.
Then the sheep's strong horns knocked
him over and rolled him outside.

The pig began to stamp on the wolf.
One goose began to bite his ear and nose.
The other goose pulled the hair that hung
down from his chin.

The rooster flew up to the housetop
and squawked, "Bite him! Bite him!
Bite him!"

What a loud squawking and squealing there was! All those animals made the loudest squawks and squeals ever heard in the wild woods.

The wolf had such a bad scare that he made no cries at all. He picked himself up and ran home as fast as he could.

"Well!" said one of the wolf's brothers. "I never knew you to pay a shorter visit.

What happened to you? I can hardly tell who you are. You have bites and bumps all over you."

The smallest wolf rubbed his chin.

"Brother," he said, "your chin hasn't a hair on it. Tell me what happened. Did you visit those silly farm animals?"

"Yes," cried the scared wolf. "I have been having a terrible time. You should have been there yourself a while ago.

Those big bad animals caught me and stamped on me and tried to gobble me up.

All the time they roared like lions. They called, 'Bite him! Bite him!'"

The whole wolf family was scared!

"Oh, dear me!" said the smallest wolf. "If those mean farm animals are going to stay here, we must move away."

So the wolf family moved at once.

The biggest wolf never forgot his visit. The smallest one always remembered how mean farm animals can be.

And the whole wolf family always remembered why they had to move.

From that day on, the five friends lived together in their home in the wild woods. They were as happy and gay as could be.

TO THE TEACHER

The new *More Friends and Neighbors*, Book 2², with its accompanying *Guidebook* and *Think-and-Do Book*, continues The New Basic Reading Program for the primary grades. It is designed for approximately one semester's use whenever the child has successfully completed the new *Friends and Neighbors*.

The new *More Friends and Neighbors* has a total vocabulary of 879 words. Of these, 315 words are new in this book; 229 were introduced in Book 2¹; 177 were introduced in Book 1²; 100 were new in the Primer; and the remaining 58 were introduced in the Pre-Primers.

No page introduces more than two of the 315 new words. The first five uses of each new word are bunched for easy mastery; there is no gap of more than five pages between any two of these first five uses. Thereafter, at spaced intervals, at least five more uses of each word occur. Each of the 564 words that were introduced in preceding books of The New Basic Reading Program is also used a minimum of five times in the new *More Friends and Neighbors*.

The 315 new words in this book are listed below. The following forms of known words are not counted as new (including those forms made by doubling the final consonant of the root word): forms made by adding or dropping the inflectional endings *s*, *d*, *ed*, and *ing;* possessives; forms made by adding or dropping the suffix *-y;* compounds made up of known words; contractions in which no more than one letter is omitted. Homographs are not counted as separate words; for example, if *tap* meaning "the sound of a light blow" has been introduced, *tap* meaning "faucet" is not counted as a separate word. Syllables and letters that represent sounds are not counted as new.

The red asterisks indicate 181 words that children can attack independently by applying the word-attack skills developed in The New Basic Reading Program. The type of analysis that children can use in unlocking each attack word is indicated in the *Guidebook* for the new *More Friends and Neighbors*.

VOCABULARY LIST

Unit I	11 ice*	17 hurt	23 .....
	skates*	slide*	24 .....
5 Oak	12 smile*	18	25 Betty
6 waved	13 foot	19 sliding	Valentine's
7 suddenly	14 lunch	20 sleds*	26 fixing*
8 horns*	end	21 wet*	paper
9 legs*	15	22 pan*	27 box*
10	16 arms*	matter	shut*

236

28 .....
29 word *
30 shoes
   bought *
31 steps *
   left *
32 corner
   count
33 policeman
   lifting *
34 happen
35 riding *
36 week *
   saved *
37 pictures
   clowns *
38 dimes *
   real
39 paid *
40 .....
41 Wags *
   Molly *
42 wondered
   does
43 slowly
   men *
44 .....
45 station
   bring *
46 stood *
47 while *
   hear *
48 roller
49 barked *
   quiet
50 summer
51 hoe *
   weeds *
52 Aunt
   resting *
53 past *
   cream *
54 been

55 .....
56 drive *

Unit II

57 .....
58 Sandy *
   often
59 pen *
   grunting
60 queer
   pointed
61 cool *
   bad *
62 I've
63 goes *
64 farmer
   listen
65 bugs *
   hay *
66 detour
   longer
67 cries *
   quit
68 .....
69 quickly *
70 Sam *
   hotter
71 Kitty
   trot *
72 shortest
   middle
73 joke *
   shorter
74 mouth
   bumpety
75 cart *
   David
76 still *
   magic
77 ear *
   whispered

78 should *
   seems *
79 hold *
   wooden
80 .....
81 wash
   Penny
82 face *
   trip *
83 above
84 voice
   babies *
85 living
   almost
86 Banks *
   knocked
87 crack *
   wren
88 screaming *
   carry
89 alone
90 forth *
91 excited
92 Skip *
   smart *
93 loud
   supper
94 kitchen
   chairs *
95 followed
   tap *
96 .....
97 chatter *
   maple
98 learn
   tiny
99 warm
   branch *
100 hiding *
    toward
101 poor *
102 friendly *
    yourself

Unit III

103 .....
104 yet *
    pooh
105 geese *
    turtle
106 jay *
    woodpeckers
107 sound *
    young
108 wise *
    filled *
109 teacher *
    waddled
110 neck *
    forgot
111 sing *
    butter
112 teaching *
    roses *
113 write *
    squawk *
114 became
115 bright *
    taste *
116 only
    few *
117 flowers
    same *
118 perhaps
119 bed *
    feathers
120 danced
    squeaky *
121 smiling *
    sad *
122 tonight
    taking *
123 gate *
    squealed *
124 most
    pink *

125	proud *	147	pond *	174	.....		Unit V
	afternoon		drinks *	175	apron	205	.....
126	village	148	fiddle	176	carried *	206	sly *
127	rub *		earn *	177	everybody		caught
	scrub *	149	.....	178	errand	207	river
128	dust *	150	branches *		vines *		bite *
	wings *	151	need *	179	nickels	208	wide *
129	dress *		shall		pins *		hung *
	sure	152	tall *	180	groceries *	209	mean *
130	lay *		forest	181	storekeeper *		ago
	table	153	machine		strong *	210	wife *
131	such *		moving *	182	sudden *		churn *
	these *	154	else		sell *	211	terrible
132	plenty	155	angry	183	present	212	stamped *
	done	156	.....	184	covered		roared *
133	engine	157	.....		truck *	213	rope *
	wheat *	158	.....	185	.....		roof *
134	hard *			186	.....	214	bridge
	easy		Unit IV	187	you'll	215	.....
135	flour *			188	chin *	216	great
	bread	159	.....		yesterday		gruff *
136	bags *	160	boards *	189	even	217	.....
	lazy		hammer	190	strange *	218	ugly
137	years *	161	heavy		caps *		troll
	harder *		whole	191	.....	219	trap *
138	kept *	162	noon *	192	having *		gobble
	surely *		stairs *		given *	220	.....
139	Easter	163	reach *	193	.....	221	.....
	hive *	164	hardly *	194	pumpkin	222	.....
140	path *		helper *		taken *	223	.....
141	tweet *	165	boxes *	·195	grew *	224	smaller *
	leafy *		might *	196	hope *	225	smallest *
142	gay *	166	louder *		believe	226	wild
143	meet *		grocery	197	.....	227	.....
	fairy	167	straight *	198	.....	228	sheep *
144	dancing *	168	loudest *	199	.....	229	.....
	stars *	169	part *	200	weather	230	.....
145	touch	170	myself		colder *	231	.....
	change *	171	.....	201	.....	232	wolf
146	really *	172	clock *	202	.....	233	.....
	eaten *		baking *	203	remember	234	.....
		173	oven	204	since	235	.....

238

ACKNOWLEDGMENTS

For permission to adapt and use copyrighted material, grateful acknowledgment is made to the following:

To the author and *Jack and Jill* for "Patty Helps Herself" from "Learning to Ice Skate" by Jo Minner; to David C. Cook Publishing Company and *Dew Drops* for "Fun on the Ice" from "Buffet's First Ice" by Mildred Comfort; to Shepard and Lawrence, Inc., for "Fun in the Snow" from "When the Snow Came" by Mark Francis in Volume I of *Book Trails;* to the author and *Child Life* for "A Big Surprise" from "The Mixed Up Christmas" by Vivian E. Laubach, copyright, 1948, by Child Life, Inc.; to the author for "Bobby's New Shoes" from "One of Billy's Best Friends" by Blanche Heywood in *Junior Home Magazine;* to *The Grade Teacher* for "Which Circus?" from "Donny Goes to the Wrong Circus" by Marjorie Williams; to the author for "Wags" adapted from *Penny and Peter* by Carolyn Haywood, copyright, 1946, by Harcourt, Brace and Company, Inc.; to the author for "A Trick for Wags" from a story of the same name by Grace Black; to the authors for "Tom's Wish" from "Billy Goes to Work" from *Farm Stories* by K. and B. Jackson, copyright, 1946, by Simon and Schuster, Inc., and Artists and Writers Guild, Inc., reprinted by permission.

To the author and *Children's Activities* for "A Trick on Sandy" from "The Cookies" by Ruth Bishop Juline; to the author for "Friends for a Farmer" from "Mr. Bob White's Nest" by Robert L. Grimes; to the author and Houghton Mifflin Company for "Sleepy Sam" from "The Drive Without End" in *Calico* by Ethel C. Phillips; to the author and *Child Life* for "Stop and Go" from "The Bureaus with Ears" by Edith Armstrong, copyright, 1929, by Rand McNally and Company; to the author and *The Christian Science Monitor* for "The Kitten That Worked" from "Penny Finds a Partner" by Anne Halladay; to the author and *American Childhood* for "Home Wanted!" from "Charla and the Wrens" by Ruth Kersey; to *The Youth's Companion* (combined with *The American Boy*) for "How Skip Found Joe" from "How Boss Got Home" by Marian Willard; to the author for "The Squirrel's Policeman" from "Little Brother of the Squirrels" by Patten Beard.

To the author and *Pictures and Stories* for "Billy Ground Hog Finds Spring" from "Sammy Woodchuck Finds Spring" by George S. Lookabaugh; "Mrs. Goose Forgets": adapted and reprinted by permission of Frederick A. Stokes Company, Inc., from *Mrs. Goose of Animaltown* by Miriam Clark Potter. Copyright, 1938, by Miriam Clark Potter; to the author and *Children's Activities* for "The Old Woman's New Hat" from "The Little Old Woman and Her New Bonnet" by Doris Bateman; to *Children's Activities* for "Little Mouse Dances" from "The Dancing

Mouse" by Elizabeth Upham; to the author for "The Little Engine" from "The Pony Engine" by Mabel C. Bragg; to The John Day Company, Inc., for "The Easter Rabbit" from "The Little White Bunny and How He Changed" in *The Two Bobbies* by Dorothy Baruch; to the author and *Child Life* for "Second Helpings" from the story of the same name by Elizabeth Ireland, copyright, 1948, by Child Life, Inc.; to the author for "Mr. Hurry Changes Things" from *Mr. Dawson Had a Farm* by R. O. Work, copyright, 1951, and used by special permission of the publishers, the Bobbs-Merrill Company, Inc.

To the author and *Jack and Jill* for "The Two Workmen" from "The Little Workman" by Ruth Anne Korey; to the author and *The Christian Science Monitor* for "Molly Plays a Joke" from "The Baby Who Would Be Himself" by Henry Beston; to the author and *American Childhood* for "Aunt Susan's Clock" from "Why the Clock Held up Its Hands" by Maud Lindsay; to the author and the George G. Harrap & Company, Ltd., for "The Errand Girl" from "Milly-Molly-Mandy Goes Errands" in *Milly-Molly-Mandy Stories* by Joyce Lancaster Brisley; to *Children's Activities* for "The Birthday Present" from "Billy's Valentine" by Grace and Olive Barnett; to the author and *Jack and Jill* for "The New Teacher" from "Miss Topsy Turvy" by Irene U. Hartwell; to David C. Cook Publishing Company and *Dew Drops* for "Jay's Pumpkin" from "Everybody's Pie" by Dorothy Arno Baldwin; and to the author and *Children's Activities* for "The Christmas Sled" from "Rory and the Red Sled" by Jean Wyatt.

ILLUSTRATIONS

The pictures in this book were made by Connie Moran, Walter Ohlson, Walter Oschman, Ellen Segner, Keith Ward, and Jack White.